Fenton Glass:
The Third Twenty-Five Years

Comprehensive Price Guide
—1995—

Compiled by members of
The Fenton Art Glass Collectors of America

The Glass Press, Inc.
dba Antique Publications
Post Office Box 553 • Marietta, Ohio 4575

Color Codes:

AB1	Apple Blossom	1/1960 - 7/1961
AB2	Apple Blossom	7/1969 - 12/1970
AG	Apple Green (Overlay)	1961 only
AO	Autumn Orange (Gold Aventurine)	7/1964 - 12/1967
AR	Amber (Antique Amber - See CA)	1/1959 - 12/1980
AW	Antique White	1980
BA	Blue Satin	1973 - 1984
BB	Bluebells on Hobnail	1971 - 1972
BC1	Blue Crest	1963 only
BC2	Bluebirds on Custard	1977 - 1979
BD1	Burmese with Transfer Leaves	1970 - 1972
BD2	Blue Dogwood on Cameo Satin	1980 - 1982
BF	Barber (Pulled Feathers)	1975
BH	Bittersweet Hanging Hearts	1975
BJ	Pekin Blue II	1968 - 1969
BK	Black	1968 - 1976; 1981 - 1982
BK1	Black Crest	1970
BL	Blue Roses on Blue Satin	1978 - 1983
BM	Blue Mist	1964 only
BN1	Blue Opaline	1960 only
BN2	Brown Rose	1973
BO	Blue Opalescent	1959 - 1964; 1979 - 1981
BQ	Blue Roses on Custard	1981
BR	Burmese	1970 - present
BU	Blue	1960 - 12/1973
BV	Powder Blue Overlay	1961 - 1962
BW	Black and White	1962 - 12/1977
BY	Butterflies	1977 - 1978
CA	Colonial Amber	1962 - 1980
CB	Colonial Blue	1962 - 12/1979
CD	Daisies on Cameo Satin	7/1978 - 1983
CG	Colonial Green	1963 - 12/1976
CH	Holly on Custard	7/1972 - 1981
CI	Custard Hanging Heart	1976 only
CK	Chocolate	1/1976 - 12/1976
CL	Coral	1961 only
CM	Cranberry Mist	1965
CN	Original Formula Carnival	1970 - 1973
CO1	Orange Carnival	7/1971 - 12/1973
CO2	Cameo Opalescent	1979 - 1982
CP	Colonial Pink	1962 - 1968
CR	Cranberry Opalescent	1956 - present
CS	Crystal Satin	1972 - 1974
CT	Custard	1975 - 1976
CU	Custard Satin	1/1972 to present
CV1	Barber (Cascade)	1975
CV2	Christmas Morn	1978 Christmas Classic
CW	Cardinals in Winter	7/1977 - 1979
CY	Crystal	1956 - present
DA	MI Flower w/artificial daisies	1/1975
DB	Decorated Burmese	1973 - 1980
DC	Daisies on Custard	1975 - 1982
DH	Holly on Milk	7/1971 - 1975
DR	Chocolate Roses on Cameo Satin	1979 - 1982

Color Codes:

DV	Decorated Violets	1969 - 1984
EG	Egg Paperweight	7/1976
FC	Flame Crest	1963 only
FL	Florentine Treatment	1980
FO	French Opalescent	1956 - 1968
GB	Aventurine Green with Blue	1964 - 1968
GC	Gold Crest	1963 - 12/1964
GD	Goldenrod	7/1956 - 12/1956
GH	Going Home	1980 Christmas Classic
GL	Gold on White Satin	1975 - 12/1978
GN	Green (code changed to GR)	1/1960
GO	Green Opalescent	7/1959 - 7/1961
GR1	Green (code changed to GT 1977)	7/1961 - 12/1962
GR2	Green Rose (decoration)	1973 - 1975
GT	Springtime Green	1977 - 1978
HA	Honey Amber	1/1961 - 12/1967, lamps 1977 - 78
HB1	Satin Blue Overlay	Lamps - 7/1976
HB2	Butterfly w/Blossom on HA	Lamps - 1977 - 1978
IB	Independence Blue Carnival	7/1974 - 12/1976
JA	Jade Green	Early 1980 only
JB	Jamestown Blue (Cased)	1957 - 1958
JM	Jamestown Blue with Milk	1957 - 1958
JO	Jonquil Yellow	1968 - 1969
JT	Jamestown Blue Transparent	1957 - 1958
LB	Barber (Labyrinth)	1975
LC1	Cased Lilac	7/1955 - 6/1956
LC2	Log Cabin on Custard	1977 - present
LM	Lime Green	7/1974 - 12/1976
LN	Lavender Satin	1977 - 1978
LR	Love Rose on Ruby	1979 - 1980
LS	Limited Sherbet	1973 - 1980
LW	Love Rose on White	1979 - 1980
MB	Blue Marble	1970 - 12/1973
MD	Milk Decorated	1971 - 1972
MG	Milk with Dark Green	1953 - 12/1956
MI	Milk Glass	Continuous production
MR	Milk Glass with Roses	1/1977
NB	New Born	1980 Mother's Day
NC	Nature's Christmas	1979 Christmas Classic
OB1	Opaque Blue	1/1962 - 12/1965
OB2	Blue Overlay	Lamps only 1967 and 1971
OE	Orange Satin	1/1968 - 6/1968
OG	Shelley Green Overlay	1967 only
OM	The Old Mill	1979 - 1980
OP	Opal	1969 only
OR	Orange	1963 - 12/1977
PA	Plated Amberina	1/1962 - 12/1963
PB	Peach Blow	1939, 1952 - 1957
PC	Peach Crest	1940 - 12/1969
PF	MI Flower w/pink flowers	1/1975
PK	Peking Blue	Early 1980 only
PN	Pink Opaline	1960 only
PO	Plum Opalescent	1/1959 - 12/1962
PR1	Purple Rose	1973 - 1974

Color Codes:

PR2	Patriot Red	1976 only
PY	Pink Anemone or Pink Blossom	1973 - present
RB	Rose Burmese	1971 - 1980
RC	Roses in Custard	1977 - 1983
RD	Roses on Ruby	1979 - present
RE	Rosalene	1/1967 - 1978; 1989
RH	Holly on Ruby	7/1972 - 1982
RM	Rose Mist	1964 - 1965
RN	Ruby Iridescent	1967 - 1977
RO	Ruby Overlay	1956 - 1974
RP	Rose Pastel	1954 - 1957
RS	Rose Satin	1974 - 1977
RU	Ruby	1966 - present
RW	Roses on Milk	1974 - 1975
SB	Satin Blue Overlay	Lamps - 1976 - 1977
SC	Silver Crest	1940 - 1986
SH	Satin Honey Amber	Lamps - 7/1976
SJ	Silver Jamestown	1/1957 - 12/1959
SL	Silver on White Satin	1975 - 1976
SR2	Satin Rosalene	7/1976 - 1977
SR1	Silver Rose	1956 - 1957
SS	Sunset on Cameo Satin	1980 - 1982
ST1	Silver Turquoise	1956 - 1958
ST2	Barber (Summer Tapestry)	1975
TB	Hand-rubbed Blue Satin on MI	7/1969; 1980 - 1982
TG	Hand-rubbed Green Satin on MI	7/1969
TH	Turquoise Hanging Heart	1976 only
TO	Topaz Opalescent	1959 - 1962; 1980
TN	Antique Brown	1980 - 1982
TS	Hand-rubbed Brown Satin on MI	7/1969
TU	Turquoise	1955 - 1958
VC	Egg "Violets on Custard"	1973 - 1974
VE	Crystal Velvet	1977 - present
VR	Velva Rose	1980 - 1982
WB	Blue Roses	7/1972; 1977 - 1978
WD	White Daisies (on Black)	1972 - 1976
WR	Wild Rose	1961 - 1962
WS	White Satin	1/1972 - present
WT	Wisteria	1977 - 1978
YF	MI Flower w/Yellow, White Flowers	1/1975
YN	Yellow Opaline	1960
YR	Yellow Roses	7/1969

R	Rare
VR	Very Rare
S	Scarce

NOTE: The numerals 1 and 2 after some of the color codes were added by the publisher to distinguish colors in the following price guide.

FRONT COVER:

Description	Ware No.	Value & Rarity
Fairy Light, one piece	7392 RB	200.00
Heart-shaped Candy Box	8200 CB	105.00
Handled Basket, 11"	6437 RG	97.00
Flowered Footed Comport	8422 RE	50.00
Lavabo Set, three piece	3867 HA	225.00

BACK COVER:

Description	Ware No.	Value & Rarity
Jefferson Comport, Favrene	8476	500.00 VR
Blue Feather Vase, 7-1/2"	0004 BF	135.00
Covered Ogee Candy Box	9394 RE	95.00
Tulip Vase	7255 RB	95.00
Student Lamp, 21"	3807 MI	130.00

Page 65

A	Basket	7237 CW	45.00
B	Basket	7237 ST	55.00
C	Epergne	7308 AB1	275.00 S
D	Basket	7237 BK1	85.00 S
E	Melon Rib Vase	7451 BK1	50.00 S
F	Cigarette Lighter	9198 CG	12.00
G	Cruet	2473 JT	90.00
H	Cruet	2473 RO	75.00
I	Oil Bottle	3869 CR	60.00
J	Vase	6455 AG	50.00
K	Vase	6058 LCI	65.00
L	Handled Jug	6068 LCI	68.00
M	Vase	6056 SJ	45.00
N	Candy Jar	3883 CR	75.00
O	Hobbs Covered Candy Jar	323	N/A
P	Slipper	3995 WT	32.00
Q	Oval Basket	1939 CA	12.00
R	Tray	6209 MI	18.00
R	Salt & Pepper Shakers	6206 JT	50.00/pr.
R	Mustard	6289 JT	40.00
S	Creamer	2461 JT	35.00

Pages 66 through 95

Item	Description	Pattern	Ware No.	Value & Rarity
Page 66				
1	Basket, 9"	Cactus	3439 TO	165.00
2	Tall Vase	Cactus	3452 TO	65.00
3	Epergne	Cactus	3401 TO	175.00
4	Medium Vase	Cactus	3461 TO	62.00
5	Vase, 5"	Cactus	3454 TO	35.00
6	Footed Bowl (Compote)	Cactus	3422 TO	148.00
7	Goblet	Cactus	3445 TO	30.00
8	Footed Nut Dish	Cactus	3428 TO	38.00
9	Candleholder	Cactus	3474 TO	60.00/pr.
10	Basket, 7"	Cactus	3437 TO	110.00
11	Fan Vase, 6"	Cactus	3459 TO	100.00
12	Salt Shaker	Cactus	3406 TO	35.00/pr.
13	Cruet with Stopper	Cactus	3463 TO	140.00
14	Banana Bowl	Cactus	3425 TO	75.00
15	Handled Bonbon	Cactus	3435 TO	40.00
16	Covered Sugar & Creamer	Cactus	3408 TO	65.00/set
17	Sugar & Creamer	Cactus	3404 TO	55.00
18	Covered Butter Dish	Cactus	3477 TO	70.00
Page 67				
19	Vase, 10"	Coin Dot	1422 TO	130.00
20	Vase, 8"	Coin Dot	1459 CR	80.00
21	Vase, 8"	Coin Dot	1477 CR	85.00
22	Vase, 6"	Coin Dot	1440 CR	65.00
23	Bowl, 8-1/2"	Coin Dot	1438 CR	65.00
24	Hurricane Globe	Coin Dot	170 CR	150.00
25	Vase, 8"	Coin Dot	1458 TO	130.00
26	Vase, 7"	Coin Dot	1441 TO	75.00
27	Vase, 6"	Coin Dot	1456 CR	75.00
28	Vase, 4-1/2"	Coin Dot	1454 CR	50.00
29	Rose Bowl, 4"	Coin Dot	1425 CR	50.00
30	Basket, 7"	Coin Dot	1437 CR	90.00
31	Ivy Vase	Coin Dot	1448 TO	60.00
32	Vase, 6"	Coin Dot	1466 TO	60.00
33	Cruet	Coin Dot	1473 TO	125.00
34	Rose Bowl, 4"	Coin Dot	1425 TO	60.00
35	Vase, 4-1/2"	Coin Dot	1454 TO	55.00
36	Vase, 7-1/2"	Coin Dot	1457 TO	80.00
Page 68				
37	Tall Vase	Hobnail	3759 GO	45.00
38	Deep Basket, 7"	Hobnail	3637 CR	190.00
39	Tumbler, 12 oz.	Hobnail	3947 CR	40.00
40	Ice Lip Jug, 70 oz.	Hobnail	3664 CR	190.00
41	Candleholder	Hobnail	3870 CR	140.00/pr.
42	Vase, 8"	Hobnail	1447 CR	85.00
43	Vase, 10"	Hobnail	189 CR	140.00

44	Comport	Hobnail	3728 GO	30.00
45	Candleholder	Hobnail	3974 GO	50.00/pr.
46	Miniature Epergne Set	Hobnail	3801 GO	90.00
47	Footed Candy Jar	Hobnail	3887 GO	50.00
48	Comport	Hobnail	3727 GO	35.00
49	Bud Vase, 8"	Hobnail	3756 GO	25.00
50	Vase, 6"	Hobnail	1456 LO	100.00
51	Vase, 4-1/2"	Coin Dot	1454 LO	50.00
52	Ivy Vase	Coin Dot	1448 CR	45.00
53	Vase, 5"	Coin Dot	1450 CR	50.00
54	Vase, 6"	Coin Dot	1440 CR	65.00

Page 69

55	Pitcher Vase	Hobnail	3760 PO	165.00
56	Wine Glass	Hobnail	3843 PO	38.00
57	Handled Wine Decanter	Hobnail	3761 PO	225.00
58	Oval Basket, 12"	Hobnail	3839 PO	200.00
59	Syrup Jug, 12 oz.	Hobnail	3762 PO	80.00
60	Vase, 6"	Hobnail	3750 PO	75.00
61	Medium Vase	Hobnail	3758 PO	75.00
62	Tall Vase	Hobnail	3759 PO	95.00
63	Footed Bowl, 10"	Hobnail	3731 PO	110.00
64	Candleholder	Hobnail	3974 PO	90.00
65	Footed Candy Jar	Hobnail	3887 PO	115.00
66	Bud Vase, 8"	Hobnail	3756 PO	30.00
67	Basket, 7"	Hobnail	3837 PO	110.00
68	Comport	Hobnail	3728 PO	50.00
69	Vase, 9"	Hobnail	3755 PO	100.00
70	4-piece Epergne Set	Hobnail	3801 PO	225.00
71	Candle Bowl	Hobnail	3771 PO	65.00
72	Candle Bowl, Interior	Hobnail	3771 PO	65.00
73	Crimped Bowl, 9"	Hobnail	3924 PO	75.00

Page 70

74	Footed Candy Box	Hobnail	3784 CG	20.00
75	Candy Box	Hobnail	3668 GT	22.00
76	Cigarette Lighter	Hobnail	3692 CG	10.00
77	Vase, 4"	Hobnail	3952 CG	9.00
78	Miniature Candle Bowl	Hobnail	3873 CG	10.00
79	Slipper	Hobnail	3995 GO	25.00
80	Footed Comport	Hobnail	3920 TO	75.00
81	Ribbon Candy Bowl	Hobnail	3730 TO	65.00
82	Ivy Bowl	Hobnail	3726 TO	42.00
83	Vase, 5"	Hobnail	3850 TO	50.00
84	Candleholder	Hobnail	3974 TO	60.00/pr.
85	Slipper	Hobnail	3996 TO	22.00
86	Candle Bowl	Hobnail	3771 TO	50.00
87	Planter, 10"	Hobnail	3779 BK	22.00
88	Planter, 8-1/2"	Hobnail	3697 BK	20.00
89	Fairy Light	Hobnail	3608 CB	18.00
90	Oval Nut Dish	Hobnail	3633 CB	13.00

Page 71

91	Candleholder, 10"	Hobnail	3774 AR	35.00/pr.
92	Apothecary Jar	Hobnail	3689 CA	50.00
93	Basket, 7"	Hobnail	3837 CA	22.00
94	Footed Comport	Hobnail	3628 RU	18.00
95	Bell	Hobnail	3667 RU	22.00
96	Basket, 12"	Hobnail	3734 RU	60.00
97	Covered Butter Bowl	Hobnail	3802 CA	15.00
98	Squat Jug	Hobnail	3965 AR	25.00
99	Vase, 7"	Hobnail	3654 CA	9.00
100	3-piece Fairy Light	Hobnail	3804 CA	30.00
101	Nut or Ice Cream Dish	Hobnail	3650 CA	10.00
102	3-Toed Bowl, 8-1/2"	Hobnail	3724 AR	25.00
103	Ball Ashtray	Hobnail	3648 RU	15.00
104	Miniature Creamer	Hobnail	3665 OR	10.00
105	3-Piece Ashtray Set	Hobnail	3610 RU	20.00/set
106	Same as 105			
107	Same as 105			
108	Basket, 7"	Hobnail	3837 RU	35.00
109	Boot	Hobnail	3992 RU	12.00

Page 72

110	Vase, 11"	Hobnail	3752 WR	100.00
111	Vase, 8"	Hobnail	3858 WR	83.00
112	Vase, 8"	Hobnail	3856 WR	55.00
113	Vase, 5-1/2"	Hobnail	3656 WR	45.00
114	Syrup Jug, 12 Oz.	Hobnail	3762 WR	55.00
115	Vase, 11-1/2"	Bubble Optic	1359 WR	175.00
116	Vase, 7-1/2"	Wild Rose w/Bowknot	2857 WR	75.00
117	Vase, 5"	Wild Rose w/Bowknot	2855 WR	70.00
118	Vase, 6"	Jacqueline	9156 WR	85.00
119	Vase	Wheat	5858 WR	70.00
120	Vase, 5-1/2"	Bubble Optic	1350 WR	60.00
121	Vase, 7-1/2"	Bubble Optic	1356 WR	65.00
122	Covered Candy Box		6080 WR	115.00
123	Vase, 5-1/2"	Hobnail	3850 OB	52.00
124	3-Piece Lavabo Set	Hobnail	3867 OB	225.00
125	Same as 124			
126	Syrup Jug, 12 Oz.	Hobnail	3762 OB	50.00

Page 73

127	Pinch Vase	Bubble Optic	1358 HA	60.00
128	Vase, 5"	Hobnail	3850 HA	45.00
129	Syrup Jug, 12 Oz.	Hobnail	3762 HA	55.00
130	Vase, 7-1/2"	Wild Rose w/Bowknot	2857 CL	68.00
131	Covered Candy Box		6080 CL	115.00
132	Vase, 11-1/2"	Bubble Optic	1359 CL	150.00
133	Vase, 5"	Hobnail	3850 CL	60.00
134	Syrup Jug, 12 Oz.	Hobnail	3762 CL	60.00
135	Vase, 6"	Hobnail	3856 CL	60.00
136	Vase	Wheat	5858 AG	45.00

137	Vase, 7-1/2"	Wild Rose w/Bowknot	2857 AG	50.00
138	Pitcher, 48 Oz.	Jacqueline	9166 AG	75.00
139	Vase, 8-1/2"	Bubble Optic	1352 GV	70.00
140	Vase, 7-1/2"	Bubble Optic	1357 GV	58.00
141	Creamer & Sugar Set	Jacqueline	9100 AG	55.00
142	Same as 141			
143	Salt & Pepper	Jacqueline	9106 AG	30.00/pr.
144	Vase, 5-1/2"	Bubble Optic	1350 AG	48.00
145	Syrup Jug, 12 Oz.	Bubble Optic	3762 AG	45.00

Page 74

146	Footed Bowl		7330 ST	65.00
147	Candleholder		7271 ST	38.00/pr.
148	Basket, 7"		7237 ST	55.00
149	Vase, 11-1/2"		3264 TU	45.00
150	Footed Cake plate		7213 SR	52.00
151	Basket, 7"		7237 SR	40.00
152	Handled Relish		7333 SR	35.00
153	Bowl, 7"		7227 SR	23.00
154	Bonbon, 5-1/2"		7225 SR	12.00
155	Hurricane Lamp		7290 ST	70.00
156	Handled Jug, 9"		7264 LCI	75.00
157	Footed Comport		7228 ST	20.00
158	Bonbon, 5-1/2"		7225 ST	10.00
159	Candleholder	Hobnail	3974 GP	30.00/pr.
160	Crimped Bowl, 9"	Hobnail	3924 GP	30.00

Page 75

161	Bowl, 13"		7223 GD	170.00
162	Candleholder		7272 GD	135.00
163	Vase, 12"		7265 GD	142.00
164	Condiment Set		6909 GD	172.00
165	Vase, 12"		7262 SJ	85.00
166	Bowl, 8-1/2"		7338 JB	55.00
167	Vase, 6"		7456 JB	43.00
168	Vase, 5"	Ribbed Pillar	9055 JB	40.00
169	Barber Bottle		7471 JB	80.00
170	Barber Bottle		2471 JT	75.00
171	Candy Box		6080 JT	80.00
172	Footed Ivy Ball		1021 JM	45.00
173	Bowl, 7"		7227 SJ	35.00
174	Vase, 6-1/2"		6058 SJ	50.00
175	Basket, 7"		7237 SJ	65.00
176	Tulip Vase, 8"		7250 SJ	64.00

Page 76

177	Vase, 11"		6458 AO	95.00
178	Handled Basket, 11"		6437 AO	120.00
179	Vase, 11"		6458 GB	95.00
180	Pitcher		6465 RG	190.00
181	Square Vase, 7"		6452 RM	68.00

182	Vase, 14"		6459 RM	110.00
183	Fan Vase, 7"		6457 AO	70.00
184	Basket, 7"		6435 AO	73.00
185	Basket, 7"		6435 GB	73.00
186	Vase, 8"		6456 RG	60.00
187	Pinch Vase, 9"		6450 RG	110.00
188	Basket, 11"		6437 RG	110.00
189	Vase, 4"		6454 GB	43.00
190	Cream Pitcher		6464 GB	55.00
191	Vase, 4"		6454 BM	47.00
192	Cream Pitcher		6464 BM	55.00
193	Vase, 5-1/2"		6455 RM	50.00
194	Vase, 5-1/2"		6455 RG	50.00

Page 77

195	Courting Lamp, Electric		1691 PA	185.00
196	Vase, 11"		6458 CM	110.00
197	Vase, 12"		7361 RO	52.00
198	Vase; 10-1/2"		1650 OB	73.00
199	Vase, 10-1/2"		1650 PA	90.00
200	Courting Lamp, Oil		1790 OR	78.00
201	Cream Pitcher		6464 CM	65.00
202	Vase, 6"		6466 CM	65.00
203	Deep Basket, 7"		1637 OB	125.00
204	Covered Candy Jar		1680 PA	150.00
205	Deep Basket, 7"		1637 PA	145.00
206	Vase, 7"		2458 RO	65.00
207	Tulip Vase, 7"	Jacqueline	9152 PN	65.00
208	Vase, 6"	Jacqueline	9156 PN	55.00
209	Tulip Vase, 7"	Jacqueline	9152 YN	55.00
210	Salt & Pepper Shakers		6006 RO	40.00/pr.
211	Creamer		2461 RO	35.00
212	Vase, 6"		2454 RO	40.00

Page 78

213	Basket, 9"	Roses	9235 MB	45.00
214	Bowl, 7"	Roses	9224 MB	25.00
215	Covered Candy Box	Roses	9284 MB	32.00
216	Handkerchief Vase	Roses	9254 MB	15.00
217	Bud Vase, 8"	Roses	9256 MB	12.00
218	Comport	Roses	9222 MB	20.00
219	Tobacco Jar	Grape & Cable	9188 MB	100.00
220	Basket, 6-1/2"	Hobnail	3736 MB	30.00
221	Footed Comport	Hobnail	3628 MB	17.00
222	Handled Bonbon	Hobnail	3706 MB	15.00
223	Footed Bowl, 10"	Hobnail	3731 MB	35.00
224	Candle Bowl	Hobnail	3872 MB	16.00
225	Candy Box	Hobnail	3886 MB	28.00
226	Large Hen on Nest		5182 MB	65.00
227	Slipper	Hobnail	3995 MB	18.00
228	Covered Slipper	Hobnail	3700 MB	30.00

Page 79

229	Vase, 8"	Bubble Optic	1358 BV	60.00
230	Vase, 7-1/2"	Wild Rose w/Bowknot	2857 BV	50.00
231	Syrup Jug	Hobnail	3762 BV	45.00
232	Vase, 6"	Hobnail	3856 BV	45.00
233	Bowl, 9"	Water Lily	8424 BA	30.00
234	Vase, 8"		9155 BA	30.00
235	Tobacco Jar	Grape & Cable	9188 BA	85.00
236	Plate	Christ Church	8280 BA	20.00
237	Candy Box	Madonna	9484 BA	30.00
238	3-Toed Bowl	Leaf & Orange Tree	8223 BA	25.00
239	Candlelight Vase	Madonna	5107 BA	30.00
240	Bell	Madonna	9467 BA	18.00
241	Cat		5165 BA	23.00
242	Donkey and Cart		5125 BA	90.00
243	Happiness Bird		5197 BA	23.00
244	Fish Paperweight		5193 BA	32.00
245	Bunny		5162 BA	20.00
246	Owl Fairy Light		5108 BA	20.00
247	Butterfly		5170 BA	20.00

Page 80

248	Basket, 11"		7434 RS	100.00
249	Small Pitcher	Melon Ribbed	7464 RS	45.00
250	Vase, 8"	Scroll Embossed	9155 RS	50.00
251	Covered Candy Box	Hobnail	3984 LS	45.00
252	Oval Comport	Pinwheel	8427 LS	25.00
253	Vase, 8"	Peacock	8257 LS	50.00
254	Crimped Comport	Water Lily	8431 LS	30.00
255	Candleholders, 6"	Orange Tree	8472 LS	40.00/pr.
256	Handled Comport	Three Fruits	8242 LS	25.00
257	Crimped Bowl	Orange Tree & Cherry	8233 LS	25.00
258	Bud Vase	Water Lily	8456 LN	33.00
259	Owl Fairy Lamp		5108 LN	45.00
260	Candy Box	Water Lily	8480 LN	60.00
261	Bowl	Basket Weave	8222 LN	30.00
262	Candy Box	Baroque	9388 LN	58.00
263	Praying Boy & Girl		5100 LN	70.00/pr.
264	Same as 263			

Page 81

265	Vase, 11"		7251 RB	125.00
266	Vase, 7"		7253 RB	125.00
267	Deep Basket, 7"		7238 RB	175.00
268	Covered Candy Box		7284 RB	200.00
269	Tulip Vase		7255 RB	95.00
270	Cruet Vase		7462 RB	95.00
271	Vase, 6-1/2"		7460 RB	95.00
272	Bud Vase		7348 RB	75.00
273	Medium Basket		7437 RB	95.00
274	2-Piece Fairy Light		7492 DB	65.00

275	Vase, 5"		7457 DB	75.00
276	Cruet with Stopper		7468 DB	150.00
277	Rose Bowl		7424 BR	70.00
278	Medium Basket		7437 BR	65.00
279	Rose Bowl		7424 BD1	65.00
280	Fairy Light		7392 BD1	150.00
281	Pitcher		7461 BD1	65.00

Page 82

282	Hurricane Lamp, 10"		7408 DC	75.00
283	Footed Candy Box		7380 DC	40.00
284	Vase, 7"		7252 DC	40.00
285	Bell		7362 OM	40.00
286	Bell		7466 CV2	35.00
287	Fairy Light		7300 CV2	35.00
288	Ham. Col. Lamp, 16"		7204 CV2	195.00
289	Donkey		5125 DC	35.00
290	Happiness Bird		5197 DC	35.00
291	Frog		5166 DC	30.00
292	Duckling		5169 DC	27.00
293	Egg		5140 BL	25.00
294	Candy Box		7484 BL	30.00
295	Duckling		5169 BL	28.00
296	3-Piece Ginger Jar		7288 BL	65.00
297	Bud Vase		9056 BL	22.00
298	3-Piece Ginger Jar		7288 LC2	115.00
299	Temple Jar		7488 LC2	50.00
300	Fairy Light		7300 LC2	45.00
301	Basket		7437 BC2	45.00
302	Bell		8267 BC2	25.00
303	Small Bird		6153 DR	20.00
304	Bell		8267 DR	20.00
305	Happiness Bird		5197 DR	25.00

Page 83

306	Vase, 7"		7252 DV	45.00
307	Small Basket		7436 DV	40.00
308	Bell		8267 DV	25.00
309	Basket, 6-1/2"		7336 DV	40.00
310	Candleholder, 6"		7474 DV	55.00
311	Footed Comport		7429 DV	39.00
312	Candleholder, 6"		7474 DV	50.00
313	Bell	Spanish Lace	3567 DV	25.00
314	Vase, 4-1/2"		7254 DV	22.00
315	Vase, 4"	Spanish Lace	3554 DV	17.00
316	Top Hat, 5"		7292 DV	65.00
317	Ash Tray		7377 DV	35.00
318	Bonbon w/Metal Handle		7498 DV	25.00
319	Footed Comport	Hobnail	3920 BB	45.00
320	Bonbon, 6"	Hobnail	3926 BB	25.00
321	Oval Basket, 12"	Hobnail	3839 BB	100.00

322	Bonbon w/Metal Handle	Hobnail	3706 BB	38.00

Page 84

323	Vase, 7"		7252 SC	40.00
324	Low Footed Comport		7329 AB1	50.00
325	Footed Cakeplate		7213 FC	120.00
326	Low Footed Comport		7329 GC	28.00
327	Bud Vase		9056 LW	17.00
328	Vase		7451 YR	33.00
329	Candleholder		7271 YR	35.00/pr.
330	Bonbon, 5-1/2"		7225 AB2	20.00
331	Candleholder		7271 AB2	30.00/pr.
332	Bell		8267 BY	25.00
333	Bud Vase		9056 BY	20.00
334	Happiness Bird		5197 CW	25.00
335	Bud Vase		9056 CW	20.00
336	Candleholder	Hobnail	3674 DH	30.00/pr.
337	Bell	Hobnail	3667 DH	25.00
338	Basket	Hobnail	3837 DH	40.00
339	Footed Comport	Hobnail	3628 DH	25.00
340	Handkerchief Vase	Hobnail	3951 DH	20.00
341	Bell	Hobnail	3667 BB	25.00
342	Fairy Light	Hobnail	3608 RW	25.00

Page 85

343	Basket		7336 AB1	100.00
344	Ash Tray		7337 AB1	38.00
345	Epergne Set		7200 PC	125.00
346	Candleholder		7272 PC	80.00/pr.
347	Vase, 8-1/2"		6059 PC	78.00
348	Handled Bonbon		7333 BK1	65.00
349	Fan Vase		7357 BK1	75.00
350	Footed Comport		7228 BC1	35.00
351	Low Footed Comport		7329 BC1	40.00
352	Salt & Pepper Shakers		7206 SC	50.00/pr.
353	Divided Basket		7339 SC	65.00
354	Candleholders		7474 FC	100.00/pr.
355	2-Tier Tidbit Top		7294 FC	45.00
356	Footed Comport		7429 FC	75.00
357	Double. Cr. Bowl, 11-1/2"		7321 FC	85.00

Page 86

358	Anniversary Bowl	Thumbprint	4484 CP	48.00
359	Bowl, 12"	Thumbprint	4427 CP	35.00
360	Goblet	Thumbprint	4445 CP	14.00
361	Jug, 34 Oz.	Thumbprint	4465 CP	52.00
362	Footed Cakeplate	Thumbprint	4411 CP	36.00
363	Basket, 8-1/2"	Thumbprint	4438 CP	35.00
364	Salt & Pepper Shakers	Thumbprint	4408 CP	22.00/pr.
365	Candleholder	Thumbprint	4470 CP	23.00/pr.
366	Sherbet	Thumbprint	4443 CP	13.00

367	Wine	Thumbprint	4444 CP	14.00
368	Chalice, 8"	Thumbprint	4448 CP	22.00
369	Footed Comport	Thumbprint	4429 CP	16.00
370	Oval Candy Box	Thumbprint	4486 CP	22.00
371	Cigarette Lighter	Thumbprint	4495 CP	15.00
	Round Ashtray, 6-1/2"	Thumbprint	4469 CP	10.00
372	Plate, 8-1/2"	Thumbprint	4417 CP	17.00
373	Oval Ash Tray	Thumbprint	4476 CP	12.00
374	Butter	Thumbprint	4477 CP	22.00
375	Covered Sugar & Creamer	Thumbprint	4403 CP	30.00/set
376	Same as 375			
377	Footed Vase, 8"	Thumbprint	4454 CP	18.00

Page 87

378	Covered Compote	Thumbprint	4484 MI	30.00
379	Basket, 8-1/2"	Thumbprint	4438 BK	30.00
380	Footed Comport	Thumbprint	4425 OR	18.00
381	Tumbler, 12 Oz.	Thumbprint	4442 CB	11.00
382	Goblet, 10 Oz.	Thumbprint	4445 RU	11.00
383	Iced Tea, 13 Oz.	Thumbprint	4449 CA	11.00
384	Tall Bud Vase	Thumbprint	4453 OR	14.00
385	Divided Relish	Thumbprint	4416 CG	15.00
386	Goblet	Roses	9246 CB	10.00
387	Owl Ring Tree		9299 CG	8.00
388	Footed Candy Box	Roses	9284 CG	15.00
389	Comport	Roses	9222 CG	12.00
390	Candy Box	Roses	9282 CP	27.00
391	Double Crimped Comport	Roses	9223 OR	8.00
392	Candleholder	Roses	9270 CB	17.00/pr.
393	Oval Vase, 4-1/2"	Roses	9251 CB	10.00
394	Ashtray	Roses	9271 CP	8.00
395	Individual Ashtray	Roses	9272 CB	6.00
396	Soap Dish	Roses	9216 CB	8.00
397	Individual Ashtray Set	Roses	9210 CB	15.00
398	Covered Sugar & Creamer	Roses	9203 MI	20.00/pr.
399	Same as 398			

Page 88

400	Ice Lip Jug, 2 Qt.	Thumbprint	4464 CB	45.00
401	Salt & Pepper Shakers	Thumbprint	4409 CB	30.00/pr. S
402	Royal Wedding Bowl	Thumbprint	4488 CB	40.00
403	4-piece Epergne Set	Thumbprint	4401 CB	45.00
404	Small Sherbet or Wine	Thumbprint	4441 CB	12.00
405	Sherbet	Thumbprint	4443 CG	9.00
406	2-piece Fairy Lite	Fine Cut & Block	9102 CG	11.00
407	Ashtray	Swirl	9176 CG	9.00
408	Sample	Fine Cut & Block		5.00
409	Bootee	Daisy & Button	1994 CG	12.00
410	Ashtray	Bird	5173 CB	30.00
411	Candy Box	Fine Cut & Block	9180 OR	16.00
412	Lighter	Valencia	8399 OR	12.00

413	Fairy Light	Santa Clause	5106 RU	30.00
414	Oval Basket	English	1939 OR	10.00
415	High Button Shoe		9195 OR	25.00
416	Boot	Daisy & Button	1990 OR	15.00
417	Bathroom Tumbler	Roses	9242 CA	8.00
418	Salt & Pepper Shakers	Roses	9206 CA	20.00/pr.

Page 89

419	Flared Bowl	Valencia	8320 CG	20.00
420	Handkerchief Vase	Valencia	8359 CG	9.00
421	Cigarette Lighter	Valencia	8344 CG	11.00
422	Footed Candy Box	Valencia	8386 CG	18.00
423	Candleholder	Valencia	8374 CG	12.00
424	Cigarette Box	Valencia	8398 CG	12.00
425	Sugar & Cream Set	Valencia	8306 CG	22.00
426	Same as 425			
427	Basket, 8"	Valencia	8388 OR	21.00
428	Sherbet	Valencia	8343 CA	11.00
429	Bud Vase	Valencia	8356 CA	8.00
430	Tall Vase	Valencia	8352 CB	15.00
431	Candy Box	Valencia	8380 CA	17.00
432	Ashtray	Valencia	8377 CA	11.00
433	Bowl, 8"	Valencia	8328 OR	11.00
434	Wine	Valencia	8344 CA	10.00
435	Goblet	Valencia	8345 CA	11.00
436	Footed Ice Tea	Valencia	8349 CB	11.00

Page 90

437	Candy Box	Knobby Bull's Eye	9385 GT	20.00
438	Fairy Light	Heart	8406 GT	18.00
439	Basket	Threaded Diamond Optic	8435 GT	20.00
440	Bell	Threaded Diamond Optic	9465 GT	16.00
441	Comport	Tree of Life	9322 GT	12.00
442	Candy Box	Colonial	8488 GT	23.00
443	Vase, 7"	Threaded Diamond Optic	8455 CG	20.00
444	Bowl, 6-1/2"	Threaded Diamond Optic	8425 CG	12.00
445	Ashtray, 5-1/2"	Free Flow	7075 CB	9.00
446	Bell	Threaded Diamond Optic	8465 WT	20.00
447	Bowl, 6-1/2"	Threaded Diamond Optic	8425 WT	15.00
448	Candy Box	Colonial	8488 WT	22.00
449	Goblet	Pineapple	9045 CP	12.00
450	Goblet	Flower Band	6345 CP	12.00
451	Goblet	Cactus	3445 CP	12.00
452	Goblet	Stippled Scroll	9145 CP	13.00
453	Goblet, 10 Oz.	Thumbprint	4445 CP	14.00
454	Footed Comport	Empress	9229 CP	10.00

Page 91

455	Comport	Roses	9222 BK	23.00
456	Footed Comport	Thumbprint	4425 BK	20.00
457	Footed Vase, 8"	Thumbprint	4454 WD	32.00

458	Footed Candy Box		7380 BK	30.00
459	Vase	Empress	8252 BK	75.00
460	Vase	Mandarin	8251 BK	85.00
461	Footed Comport	Thumbprint	4429 BK	18.00
462	Temple Jar		7488 BK	22.00
463	Fairy Light	Decision Maker	5180 BK	35.00
464	Cigarette Lighter	Thumbprint	4495 BK	12.00
465	Basket, 8-1/2"	Thumbprint	4438 BK	35.00
466	Tobacco Jar	Grape & Cable	9188 BK	95.00
467	Toothpick Holder	Panelled Daisy	8294 BK	15.00
468	Egg	Decorated	5140 WD	38.00
469	Ashtray, 6-1/2"	Thumbprint	4469 BK	12.00
470	Toothpick	Hobnail	3795 BK	10.00
471	Kitchen Salt	Hobnail	3602 BK	38.00/pr.
472	Oval Nut Dish	Hobnail	3633 BK	14.00
473	Candle Bowl	Hobnail	3872 BK	17.00

Page 92

474	Vase	Mandarin	8251 MI	70.00
475	Vase	Empress	8252 MI	65.00
476	Vase	Empress	8252 BR	135.00
477	Vase	Mandarin	8251 FO	100.00
478	Vase	Empress	8252 FO	98.00
479	Vase	Mandarin	8252 OR	120.00
480	Vase	Love Bird	8258 LS	20.00
481	Vase	Vessel of Gems	8253 OR	58.00
482	Planter Bowl	Floral	8225 RE	80.00
483	Planter Bowl	Floral	8226 CN	55.00
484	Vase	Love Bird	8258 CN	28.00
485	Girl & Fawn Bookends		5102 WS	58.00
486	Bowl	Floral	8226 MI	30.00
487	Nut Dish		8221 MI	20.00
488	Planter		8299 MI	40.00

Page 93

489	Planter/Vase	Mermaid	8254 CN	75.00
490	Vase	Atlantis	5150 CN	85.00
491	Tumbler	Butterfly & Berry	8240 CN	15.00
492	Bell	Faberge	8466 CN	25.00
493	Plate	The Cabinetmaker	9179 CN	20.00
494	Alley Cat		5177 CN	68.00
495	Candleholder	Swan	5172 CN	50.00/pr.
496	Candle Bowl, 8"	Orange Tree	9173 CN	30.00
497	Handled Bonbon	Butterfly	8230 CN	25.00
498	Comport	Pinwheel	8227 RN	30.00
499	Comport	Persian Medallion	8234 RN	30.00
500	Nut Bowl	Leaf & Orange Tree	8223 RN	25.00
501	Ceremonial Light	Chou Ting	8407 RN	60.00
502	Flared Bowl	Hearts & Flowers	8228 CN	40.00
503	Turtle Ring Tree		9199 CN	35.00
504	Butterfly		5170 CN	35.00

505	Butterfly		5170 CO1	35.00
506	Same as 505			
507	Fish Paperweight		5193 CN	38.00
508	Bowl	Butterfly & Berry	8428 RN	32.00

Page 94

509	Jefferson Comport		8476 CK	145.00
510	Jefferson Comport		8476 PR2	145.00
511	Jefferson Comport		8476 IB	115.00
512	Stein		8446 CK	30.00
513	Stein		8446 PR2	45.00
514	Patriot's Bell		8467 CK	30.00
515	Patriot's Bell		8467 PR2	30.00
516	Patriot's Bell		8467 IB	30.00
517	Eagle Plate		9418 CK	25.00
518	Eagle Plate		9418 PR2	32.00
519	Eagle Paperweight		8470 CK	30.00
520	Eagle Paperweight		8470 PR2	30.00
521	Eagle Paperweight		8470 IB	27.00
522	Patriot Planter		8499 VW	20.00
523	Patriot Planter		8499 IB	22.00

Page 95

524	Vase, 11-1/2"	Hyacinth Feather	0001 HF	200.00
525	Vase, 11"	Summer Tapestry	0005 ST	200.00
526	Vase, 10"	Hanging Heart	0007 CI	125.00
527	Vase, 10"	Hanging Heart, Iridescent	0008 TH	125.00
528	Vase, 10"	Hanging Heart	0002 TH	125.00
529	Vase, 9"	Labyrinth	0009 LA	140.00
530	Vase, 7-1/2"	Bittersweet	0003 BH	150.00
531	Vase, 7-1/2"	Cascade	0006 CV	125.00
532	Vase, 7-1/2"	Blue Feather	0004 BF	135.00
533	Vase, 9"	Labyrinth	0010 LB	150.00
534	Egg	Reddish Orange	5005 EG	100.00
535	Egg	Dark Blue	5002 EG	100.00
536	Egg	Multi-Color	5008 EG	100.00
537	Egg	Pink	5001 EG	100.00
538	Egg	Green	5007 EG	100.00
539	Egg	Light Blue	5004 EG	100.00

Page 96

540	Comport	Roses	9222 JO	70.00
541	Candy Box	Daisy & Button	1980 JO	70.00
542	Vase	Empress	8252 JO	150.00
543	Vase, 11"	Melon	7458 JO	135.00
544	Basket	Hobnail	3837 BJ	70.00
545	Footed Bowl, 10"	Hobnail	3731 BJ	50.00
546	Candy Box	Hobnail	3886 BJ	60.00
547	Boot	Daisy & Button	1990 BJ	30.00
548	Candy Box	Daisy & Button	1980 BJ	45.00
549	Basket	Hobnail	3736 BJ	55.00

550	Wise Owl	Decision Maker	5180 BJ	100.00
551	Pelican Tray		5175 JO	75.00
552	Fairy Light	Hobnail	3608 JO	55.00
553	Candleholders	Hobnail	3974 BJ	75.00/pr.
554	Candleholders	Hobnail	3974 JO	100.00/pr.
555	Boot	Daisy & Button	1990 JO	40.00

Catalog Reprints arranged in page order

Pg.#	Picture # & Year	Item	Pattern	Ware # & Color Code	Value & Rarity
97	CR 1 Jan. 1971	Double Ball Lamps 23"	Poppy	9109 CG, MI, CA	$ 110
	CR 2 Jan. 1971	Double Ball Lamps 24"	Poppy	9101 CG, CA, MI, RU	105
	CR 3 Jan. 1971	Mariner's Lamp		2700 RU, CA	325
			Violets in the Snow	4700 DV	
	CR 4 Jan. 1971	Double Ball Lamp	Roses	9202 OB, BR	350, 775,
				WS	200
	CR 5 Jan. 1971	Pillar Lamp	Roses	9201 OB,WS	300, 150
	CR 6 Jan. 1971	Pillar Lamp	Roses	9201 BR, RO	600
98	CR 7 Jan. 1951	Mariner's Lamp	Vasa Murrhine	6405 GB	410
			Decorated Violets	7404 DV	390
	CR 8 Jan. 1971	Double Ball Lamp	Roses	9207 MI	155
	CR 9 Jan. 1971	Student Lamps	Thumbprint	1408 CG, RO, CA	80, 150, 80
				1410 RO	170
	CR 10 Jan. 1971	Student Lamp	H/P Roses	7410 RB	375
		Mariner's Lamp	H/P Roses	7405 RB	500
		Fairy Light	H/P Roses	7492 RB	65
	CR 11 Jan. 1971	Student Lamp	Poppy	9107 MI	120
		Double Ball Lamp	Poppy	9108 MI	145
	CR 12 Jan. 1971	Student Lamps	Roses	9207 CG, CB, MI, CA	95-120
99	CR 13-14 July 1969	Zodiac Medallion	Aries	9360 CA	10
			Taurus	9361 RU	10
			Gemini	9362 CB	10
			Cancer	9363 CG	10
			Leo	9364 OR	10
			Virgo	9365 CY	10
			Libra	9366 CA	10
			Scorpio	9367 RU	10
			Sagittarius	9368 CB	10
			Capricorn	9369 CG	10
			Aquarius	9370 CY	10
			Pisces	9371 OR	10
	CR 14 July 1969	Zodiac Paperweights	Aries	9340 CY	20
			Taurus	9341 CY	20
			Gemini	9342 CY	20.
			Cancer	9343 CY	20
			Leo	9344 CY	20
			Virgo	9345 CY	20
			Libra	9346 CY	20

			Scorpio	9347 CY	20
			Sagittarius	9348 CY	20
			Capricorn	9349 CY	20
			Aquarius	9350 CY	20
			Pisces	9351 CY	20
	CR 15 Jan. 1977	21" Student Lamp	Rosalene Candy Stripe	2601 SR	525
		22" GWTW Lamp	Rosalene Candy Stripe	2602 SR	600
		20" Fr. Colonial Lamp	Rosalene Candy Stripe	2606 SR	525
	CR 16 Jan. 1977	22" Student Lamp	Decorated-H/P	7304 HB	200
		21-1/2" Student Lamp	Decorated-H/P	7309 MR	225
		21" Student Lamp	Decorated-H/P	7414 HB	250
100	CR 17				
	Jan. 1977-78	Happiness Bird		5197 RU	20
		3-piece Ash Tray Set		3610 RU	20
		Ball Ash Tray		3648 RU	15
		11" Vase		3752 RU	35
		Bud Vase		3756 RU	12
		Wine Decanter		3761 RU	90
		Wine Glass		3843 RU	15
		4-1/2" Vase		3854 RU	18
		Slipper		3995 RU	18
		8-1/2" Basket ✓		4438 RU	35
		20" Student Lamp	Poppy	9107 RU	150
	CR 18 Jan. 1977-78	Fairy Light	Hobnail	3608 RU	22
		Footed Comport		3628 RU	18
		Bell		3667 RU	22
		Handled Bonbon		3706 RU	20
		8" Bonbon		3716 RU	17
		12" Basket		3734 RU	60
		Footed Vase		3753 RU	20
		7" Basket		3837 RU	35
		3" Vase		3853 RU	12
		Candy Box		3886 RU	30
		Candleholder		3974 RU	20/pr.
	CR 19 Jan. 1977	5-1/2" Ash Tray	Swirl	7075 WT	8
		7-1/2" Ash Tray	Swirl	7076 WT	10
		Fairy Light	Heart	8406 WT	30
		Bowl	Threaded Diamond Optic	8425 WT	13
		7" Basket		8435 WT	38
		7" Vase		8455 WT	27
		Bell		8465 WT	20
		Candy Box	Colonial	8488 WT	23
		Comport	Tree of Life	9322 WI	18
		Candy Box	Knobby Bull's Eye	9385 WT	32
	CR 20 Jan. 1979	Bell	Lily of the Valley	8265 CO	25
		Fairy Light		8404 CO	30
		12-1/2" Cake Plate		8411 CO	60
		Basket		8437 CO	30
		Footed Bowl		8451 CO	50
		Rose Bowl		8453 CO	20

		Bud Vase		8458 CO	10
		Footed Candy Box		8484 CO	35
		Candy Box		8489 CO	20
101	CR 21-22 Jan. 1976	Mariner's Lamp, 20-1/2"	Hanging Heart	8900 TH, CI	525, 450
		Rose Bowl, 4"		8924 TH	45
		Rose Bowl, 5"		8925 CI	55
		Handled Basket		8937 TH, CI	80
		Handled Basket		8939 CI	90
		Tumbler, 10 Oz.		8940 TH, CI	40
		Vase, 4"		8954 TH	40
		Vase, 5"		8955 CI	45
		Vase, 6"		8956 CI	68
		Vase, 7"		8957 TH	68
		Vase, 8"		8958 TH, CI	75, 80
		Barber Bottle		8960 CI-	100 S
		Bottle		8961 TH	110
		Pitcher, 70 Oz.		8964 TH, CI	200
		Cruet		8969 TH, CI	110
	CR 23 Jan. 1971	3-piece Ash Tray Set	Hobnail	3610 MB	25
		Footed Comport		3628 MB	17
		Covered Slipper		3700 MB	30
		Handled Bonbon		3706 MB	15
		Footed Bowl, 10"		3731 MB	35
		Heart Shaped Relish		3733 MB	24
		Basket, 6-1/2"		3736 MB	30
		Footed Vase		3753 MB	20
		Candle Bowl		3872 MB	16
		Covered Candy Box		3886 MB	28
		Candleholder		3974 MB	20/pr.
		Slipper		3995 MB	18
	CR 24 Jan. 1971	Footed Comport	Roses	9222 MB	20
		Double Crimped Comport		9223 MB	13
		Bow, 7"		9224 MB	25
		Bowl, 9-1/2"		9225 MB	20
		Basket, 9"		9235 MB	45
		Handkerchief Vase		9254 MB	15
		Bud Vase, 8"		9256 MB	12
		Candleholder		9270 MB	20
		Ashtray		9271 MB	11
		Candy Box		9284 MB	32
102	CR 25	Fairy Light		7300 PY	30
		Basket		7437 PY	42
		Medallion Bell		8367 PY	25
		19-1/2" Student Lamp		9308 PY	155
	CR 26	7" Basket	Pink Blossom	7237 PY	40
		5-1/2" Vase		7254 PY	15
		Vase, 6"		7256 PY	20
		Footed Comport		7429 PY	30

		Pitcher		7461 PY	32
		Medallion Candy Box		8288 PY	30
		Bud Vase		9056 PY	18
	CR 27	7" Vase	Plain Burmese & Maple Leaf Decal	7252 BR, BD	40, 45
		Fairy Light		7392 BR, BD	110, 150
		8" Bowl		7422 BR, BD	60, 90
		Rose Bowl (Tightly Crimped)		7424 BR, BD	70, 65
		Basket		7437 BR, BD	45, 100
		Pitcher		7461 BR, BD	90
	CR 28	Bowl	Leaf & Orange Tree	8223 BA	25
		Comport	Pinwheel	8227 CU	25
		Comport	Persian Medallion	8234 LS	25
		Basket	Persian Medallion	8238 LS	27
		Vase	Love Bird	8258 BA	28
		Fairy Light	Persian Medallion	8408 CU	35
		Footed Candy Box	Water lily	8480 LS	42
		GWTW Lamp	Poppy	9101 CU	250
		8" Vase	Swirl	9155 RS	50
103	CR 29 Jan. 1977	7" Vase		7252 RS	50
		Basket		7437 RS	55
		36 Oz. Pitcher	Water Lily	8464 RS	75
		20" Student Lamp	Poppy	9107 RS	225
		Vase	Poppy	9154 RS	60
	CR 30 Jan. 1977	6" Vase		7451 RS	25
		11" Vase		7458 RS	85
		GWTW Lamp	Poppy	9101 RS	325
		7" Deep Basket	Poppy	9138 RS	85
		8" Vase	Swirl	9155 RS	50
	CR 31 Jan. 1976	Bowl	Leaf & Orange Tree	8223 RE	50
		Bonbon	Butterfly	8230 RE	35
		Footed Comport	Flowered	8422 RE	50
		3-Toed Bowl	Water lily	8426 RE	35
		Basket	Threaded w/diamond optic	8435 RE	60
		Candleholder	Water lily	8473 RE	60/pr.
		Cov'd Candy Box on box	Ogee	9394 RE	95
	CR 32 Jan. 1976	Fairy Light	Owl	5108 RE	35
		Happiness Bird		5197 RE	30
		Bowl	Basket Weave	8222 RE	30
		Planter Bowl	Floral	8226 RE	80
		Fairy Light	Heart	8406 RE	65
		Fan Vase		8452 RE	300
		Bell	Faberge	8466 RE	35
		Covered Candy Box	Water lily	8480 RE	75
104	CR 33 Jan. 1978	Craftsman Plate	1970 Glassmaker	9115 CN	23
			1971 Printer	9116 CN	24
			1972 Blacksmith	9117 CN	24
			1973 Shoemaker	9118 CN	24
			1974 Cooper	9119 CN	25

			1975 Silversmith	9175 CN	20
			1976 Gunsmith	9176 CN	25
			1977 Potter	9177 CN	20
			1978 Wheelwright	9178 CN	20
			1978 Cabinetmaker	9179 CN	20
	CR 34 July 1979	Christmas in America	Little Brown Church	8270 BA, CN	23
			Old Brick Church	8271 BA, CN, WS	23
			Two-horned Church	8272 BA, CN, WS	24
			St. Mary's Church	8273 BA, CN, WS	22
			Nation's Church	8274 BA, CN, WS	22
			Birthplace	8275 BA, CN, WS	28-20
			Old North Church	8276 BA, CN, WS	28-20
			San Carlos Church	8277 BA, CN, WS	22
			Holy Trinity Church	8278 BA, CN, WS	22
			San Jose Church	8279 BA, CN, WS	22
			Christ Church	8280 BA, CN, WS	20
			Mission of San Xavier Del Bac	8281 BA, CN, WA, FL	22
	CR 35 Jan. 1970	Boot	Daisy & Button	1990 CN	18
		Butterfly		5170 CN	35
		Large Hen on Nest		5182 CN	70
		Small Hen on Nest		5186 CN	35
		Fish Paperweight		5193 CN	38
		Planter Bowl		8226 CN	55
		Covered Candy Box	Strawberry	9088 CN	55
		Craftsman Plate	Glassmaker	9115 CN	23
		Oval Dish	Pansy	9125 CN	20
		Candy Box	Panelled Daisy	9185 CN	32
	CR 36 Jan. 1977	Mother's Day Plate	Madonna w/The Sleeping Child	9316 CN, BA	17, 15
			Madonna of the Goldfinch	9317 CN, BA, WS	17-12
			The Small Cowper Madonna	9318 CN, BA, WS	17-12
			Madonna of the Grotto	9319 CN, BA, WS	17-12
			Taddei Madonna	9375 CN, BA, WS	17-12
			Holy Night	9376 CN, BA, WS	17-12
			Child with Pomegranate	9377 CN, BA, WS	17-12
			Madonna or Little Madonna	9378 CN, BA, WS	17-12
			Madonna of the Rose Hedge	9379 CN, BA, WS	17-12
105	CR 37 Jan. 1967	Sugar & Creamer	Hobnail	3606 MI	20
		8-1/2" Basket		3638 MI	27
		Oval 1/4" Covered Butter Dish		3777 MI	23
		Sugar & Creamer		3915 MI	40
		Footed Covered Candy Box		3784 MI	25
		Salt & Pepper		3806 MI	15/pr.
		Footed Cake Plate		3913 MI	45
		12" Bowl		3938 MI	28
		Candleholder		3974 MI	20/pr.
	CR 38 Jan. 1967	Low Banana Bowl		3620 MI	35
		9" Footed Oval Bowl		3621 MI	25

		9-1/2" Shallow Bowl		3622 MI	45
		10-1/2" DC Bowl		3624 MI	25
		8" Oval Bowl		3625 MI	27
		8" Bowl		3626 MI	32
		3 Toed Bowl		3635 MI	14
		8" DC Bowl		3639 MI, CA	15, 10
		Low Candleholder	Hobnail	3670 MI	20/pr.
		2 Lite Candleholder	Hobnail	3672 MI	65/pr.
		Candleholder	Hobnail	3673 MI	25/pr.
		6" Candleholder	Hobnail	3674 MI	25/pr.
		Banana Bowl		3720 MI	27
		Footed Bowl		3723 MI	25
		8-1/2" Bowl		3724 MI	24
		Comport		3727 MI	14
		10" Footed Bowl	Hobnail	3731 MI	22
		Candle Bowl		3771 MI	20
		10" Candleholder		3774 MI	60/pr.
		Candleholder w/handle		3870 MI	45/pr.
		9" Bowl		3924 MI	25
		7" Bowl		3927 MI	12
		12" Bowl		3938 MI	28
		Candleholder		3974 MI	20
		Hurricane Lamp		3998 MI	45
106	CR 39 Jan. 1967	Tall Vase	Hobnail	3652 CA, CG	10, 10
				MI, CB, OR	25, 20, 15
		5" Vase		3655 MI	8
		5-1/2" Vase DC		3656 MI	14
		7" Vase		3657 MI	15
		9" Vase		3659 MI	24
		9-1/2" Planter		3690 MI	20
		Square Planter		3699 MI	12
		Epergne Set		3701 MI	50
		Hanging Bowl		3705 MI	135
		Ivy Bowl		3726 MI	15
		6" Vase (Handkerchief)		3750 MI	18
		11" Vase		3752 MI	32
		Footed Vase (Swung)		3753 MI	20
		8" Bud Vase		3756 MI, CA,	12
				CB, CG, OR	12
		Footed Ivy Vase		3757 MI	15
		Pitcher Vase		3760 MI	45
	CR 40 Jan. 1967	70 Ice Lip Jug	Hobnail	3664 CR	190
		Courting Lamp, Oil		3792 MI,	100
				CA, CB, CG	65, 65, 65
		Courting Lamp, Electric		3793 MI, CB,	100 R, 88
				CA, CG	65, 65
		Salt & Pepper		3806 CR	72/pr.
		10" Basket		3830 CR	100 S
		7" Basket		3837 CR	75
		5" Vase		3850 CR	60

		4-1/2" Vase		3854 CR	38
		8" Vase		3858 CR	75
		Cruet		3863 CR	95
		Candleholder		3870 CR	140/pr.
		9" Bowl		3924 CR	65
		7" Bowl		3927 CR	50
		12 Oz. Tumbler		3947 CR	40
	CR 41 Jan. 1967	5" Vase	Hobnail	3653, CA, CG, OR	10, 10, 10
				CB	14
		3-Toed Vase		3654 MI	12
		8" 3-Toed Vase		3658 MI	135 VR
		8-1/2" Planter		3697 MI	20
		10" Planter		3799 MI	18
		Violet Bowl		3754 MI	15
		Medium Vase		3758 MI	20
		Tall Vase		3759 MI	33
		Mini Epergne Set		3801 MI	45
		5" Vase		3850 MI	18
		4-1/2" Vase	Hobnail	3854 MI	12
		6" Vase		3856 MI	18
		8" Vase		3858 MI	30
		Lavabo		3867 MI	35
		6-1/2" DC Vase		3956 MI	14
		6-1/4" Fan Vase		3957 MI	12
		8" DC Vase		3958 MI	23
		8" Fan Vase		3959 MI	24
		4-1/2" Jardiniere		3994 MI	15
		6" Jardiniere		3996 MI	20
107	CR 42 Jan. 1967	Oval Nut Dish	Hobnail	3633 MI, CA, CB, CG	13
		8" Oval Pickle Dish		3640 MI	14
		Apothecary Jar		3689 MI, CA, CG	50, 50, 50
				CB	60
		7-Piece Juice Set		3905 MI	80
		12 Oz. Tumbler		3942 MI	15
		5 Oz. Tumbler		3945 MI	9
		9 Oz. Tumbler		3949 MI	13
		Squat Jug		3965 MI	40
		80 Oz. Jug		3967 MI	80
	CR 43 Jan. 1967	Cigarette Set	Hobnail	3603 MI, CA	40, 35
		3-piece Ashtray Set		3610 MI, CG, OR	20, 20, 20
				CA, CB	16, 16
		5" Square Ashtray		3679 MI	10
		Covered Cigarette Box		3685 MI	19
		Cigarette Lighter		3692 MI, CB, CG,	15, 15, 10
				CA, OR	13, 13
		Ashtray		3693 MI	4
		Pipe Ashtray		3773 MI	24
		Round Ashtray		3776 MI	8
		Ashtray Set (Octagon)		3810 MI	28

		No. 2 Ashtray		3877 MI	8
		Small Ashtray		3972 MI	5
		Medium Ashtray		3973 MI	7
	CR 44 Jan. 1967	Footed Peanut Dish	Hobnail	3627 MI	12
		Footed DC Comport		3628 MI	14
		Footed Nut Dish		3629 MI	10
		Footed Nut Dish		3631 MI	16
		Covered Candy Jar		3688 MI	28
		8" Bonbon		3716 MI	10
		Jelly Dish		3725 MI	10
		Comport		3728 MI	15
		Wedding Jar		3780 MI	25
		Footed Candy Box		3784 MI, CB,	25
				CA, CG, OR	20, 20, 20
		Oval Candy Box		3786 MI	20
		Candy Jar		3880 MI	25
		Candy Jar		3883 MI	30
		Footed Candy Jar		3887 MI	30
		Footed Comport		3920 MI	18
		7" Bonbon		3937 MI	12
		Footed Candy Jar		3980 MI	28
	CR 45 Jan. 1967	Oval Basket	Hobnail	3634 MI	16
		7" Deep Basket		3637 MI	49
		8-1/2" Basket		3638 MI, CA, CB,	27, 28, 29
				CG, OR	14, 27
		12" Basket		3734 MI	45
		6-1/2" Basket		3736 MI	25
		10" Basket		3830 MI	35
		4-1/2" Basket		3834 MI	15
		7" Basket		3837 MI, CA,OR	22, 22, 22
				CB, CG	25, 15
		6-1/2" Oval Basket		3838 MI	18
		12" Oval Basket		3839 MI	50
108	CR 46 Jan. 1967	Bell	Hobnail	3667 MI, CA,CG	12, 12, 12
				CB	15
		3" Vase		3853 MI	8
		Miniature Vase		3855 MI	12
		Footed Cake Plate		3913 MI	45
		8" Plate		3916 MI	38
		6" Bonbon		3926 MI	7
		4" DC Vase		3952 MI, CA,CG,	9, 9, 9
				CB, OR	10, 10
		4" Fan Vase		3953 MI	7
		Hat		3991 MI	12
		Slipper		3995 MI, CA, CB,	10, 10, 13
				CG, OR,	8, 8
				CP, RU	18, 18
	CR 47 Jan. 1967	Spoon Holder	Hobnail	3612 MI	50

		Chip 'n Dip		3703 MI	40
		Heart-Shaped Relish		3733 MI	20
		12" Divided Relish		3740 MI	25
		Handled Decanter		3761 MI	75
		54 Oz. Jug		3764 MI	50
		Sandwich Tray		3791 MI	35
		2-Tier Tidbit		3794 MI	35
		Mayonnaise Set		3803 MI	24
		Relish		3822 MI	15
		Sherbet		3825 MI	10
		Footed Ice Tea		3842 MI	15
		Wine		3843 MI	20 R
		Goblet		3845 MI	12
	CR 48 Jan. 1967	Covered Sugar & Creamer	Hobnail	3606 MI	20
		Salt & Pepper Set		3609 MI	19
		Covered Cookie Jar		3680 MI	90
		Sugar & Creamer		3708 MI	25
		12 Oz. Syrup Jug		3762 MI	24
		Oval 1/4 lb. Covered Butter		3777 MI	23
		Salt & Pepper		3806 MI	15/pr.
		Cruet		3863 MI	35
		Oil		3869 MI	20
		Mustard & Spoon		3889 MI	20
		Sugar & Creamer		3900 MI	15
		Sugar & Creamer		3901 MI	18
		Sugar & Creamer		3906 MI	22
		Oil & Vinegar (on tray)		3916 MI	38
		Sugar & Creamer (on tray) 3917 MI			29
		Oval 1/4 lb. Covered Butter		3977 MI	22
	CR 49 Jan. 1967	Kitchen Salt & Pepper	Hobnail	3602 MI	26/pr.
		Bonbon		3630 MI	8
		Nut & Ice Cream Dish		3650 MI, CA	24, 10
		70 Oz. Ice Lip Jug		3664 MI	60
		Miniature Cream		3665 MI, CA, CB,	10, 10, 10
				CG, OR	5, 10
		Covered Butter & Cheese		3677 MI	85 VR
		Ashtray		3693 MI	4
		Toothpick Holder		3795 MI, CA, CB,	10, 10, 10
				CG, OR	10, 10
		Salt & Pepper		3806 BW	15/pr.
		Condiment Set		3809 MI	65
		Jam Set		3903 MI	25
		Jam & Jelly (on tray)		3915 MI	40
		5" Star Bonbon		3921 MI	10
		Berry Dish		3928 MI	10
		Kettle		3990 MI	12
109	CR 50 Jan. 1964	Round Candle Sconce	Hobnail	M671 MI	55
		Double Candle Sconce		M672 MI	80

		Candle Sconce		M677 CR	65
		Round Planter #2		M694 MI	45
		Round Planter #1		M698 MI	45
		Rectangular Planter		M699 MI	80
	CR 51 Jan. 1975	4-piece Candelabra	Hobnail	3742 MI	85
		6-piece Candelabra Arrangement		3744 MI	80
		7" Candleholder		3745 MI	22
		Candle Epergne		3746 MI	25
	CR 52 Jan. 1976	19" Student Lamp	Hobnail	3707 MI	175
		21" Student Lamp		3807 MI	130
		Picture Frame w/Easel		9490 MI	25 S
	CR 53 Jan. 1975	Covered Jam or Candy	Hobnail	3600 MI	18
		Candy Box		3668 MI, CB,	22, 22
				CA, CG	20, 20
		Candy Jar		3688 MI	28
		Covered Slipper		3700 MI	30
		Wedding Jar		3780 MI	25
		Footed Candy Box		3784 MI	25
		Oval Candy Box		3786 MI	20
		Candy Box		3802 MI	15
		Candy Jar		3880 MI	25
		Footed Candy Box		3885 MI	25
		Candy Box		3886 MI	25
		Footed Candy Jar		3980 MI	28
		Candy Box		3984 MI	38
110	CR 54 July 1961	6" DC Vase	Silver Crest	7156 SC	18
		Footed Cakeplate		7213 SC	45
		8-1/2" Plate		7217 SC	28
		Deep Dessert		7221 SC	8
		13" Bowl		7223 SC	25
		5-1/2" Bonbon		7225 SC	10
		Sherbet		7226 SC	10
		13" Basket		7233 SC	55
		4-1/2" Vase		7254 SC	10
		8" DC Vase		7258 SC	18
		Candleholder		7272 SC	40/pr.
		Sandwich Tray		7291 SC	25
		11-1/2" DC Bowl		7321 SC	25
		Footed Square Bowl		7330 SC	50
		4-1/2" DC Vase		7354 SC	10
		6-1/4" DC Vase		7356 SC	18
		Ashtray		7377 SC	14
	CR 55 July 1961	Bowl, 11"	Sheffield	5823 SC	28
		8" Vase	Wheat	5859 SC	35
		Epergne Set (2 pc.)	Silver Crest	7202 SC	54
		Cup & Saucer		7209 SC	40/set
		Low Dessert		7222 SC	16

		10" Bowl		7224 SC	25
		7" Bowl		7227 SC	15
		Footed Nut Dish		7229 SC	10
		7" Basket		7237 SC	27
		Candleholder		7271 SC	30/pr.
		4-piece Epergne Set		7308 SC	95
		14" Bowl		7323 SC	42
		Banana Bowl		7324 SC	40
		Low Footed Comport		7329 SC	24
		Handled Relish		7333 SC	24
		Divided Relish		7334 SC	30
		6-1/2" Handled Basket		7336 SC	35
		8-1/2" Bowl		7338 SC	28
		8" Bonbon		7428 SC	8
		6" Vase		7451 SC	14
		7-1/2" Bowl		7425 SC	20
		8" Vase		7453 SC	18
	CR 56 July 1961	Low Footed Cakeplate	Silver Crest	5813 SC	32
		Banana Bowl	Sheffield	5824 SC	36
		Mayonnaise Set	Silver Crest	7203 SC	25
		10-1/2" Plate		7210 SC	25
		12-1/2" Plate		7211 SC	35
		16" Torte Plate		7216 SC	40
		8-1/2" Plate		7217 SC	28
		6-1/2" Plate		7219 SC	12
		12" Basket		7234 SC	50
		Candleholder		7274 SC	35/pr.
		2-Tier Tidbit		7294 SC	35
		Chip 'n Dip		7303 SC	45
		5-piece Epergne Set		7305 SC	120
		2-Tier Tidbit		7394 SC	35
		Footed Comport-DC		7429 SC	25
	CR 57 July 1961	Sugar & Cream	Silver Crest	7201 SC	60/pr.
		Footed Comport		7228 SC	12
		12" Vase		7262 SC	75 S
		Footed Candy Box		7280 SC	60 S
		3-Tier Tidbit		7295 SC	35
		2-Tier Tidbit		7296 SC	30
		15-piece Punch Set		7306 SC	475 R
		Shallow Bowl		7316 SC	35
		Footed Tumbler		7342 SC	45 R
		Footed Bowl		7427 SC	45
		Footed Comport—Flared		7430 SC	25
		70 Oz. Jug		7467 SC	160
		6" Candleholder		7474 SC	38/pr.
111	CR 58 1967 Supp.	Double Ball Lamp, 24"	Rose	9204 OB, WR	225, 375
		20-1/2" Ball Buffet Lamp		9205 MI, WR	140, 350
		Double Ball Lamp, 22"		9207 MI, HA,	155, 155

				OB	215
		Student Lamp, 19"		9208 MI, CB	120, 120
				CA, CG	95, 95
	CR 59	Student Lamp, 19-1/2" h.	Thumbprint	1408 RO, CG, CA	150, 80, 80
		Student Lamp, 20" h.		1410 RO, CG, CA	170, 80, 80
		Courting Lamp, Oil	Hobnail	3792 MI	100 R
		Courting Lamp, Electric		3793MI	100 S
		Student Lamp, 19" h.	Hobnail	3707 MI	175
		Student Lamp, 20" h.	Poppy	9107 MI	120
		Dble. Ball Lamp 21-1/2" h.	Poppy	9108 MI	145
		Double Ball Lamp			
		Crimped, 23" h.	Poppy	9109 MI, CA,	110, 110
				CG	110
112	CR 60 Jan. 1979	Double Ball Lamp	Spanish Lace	3509 SC	200
		Footed Comport		3522 SC	15
		8-1/2" Basket		3538 SC	45
		Bell		3567 SC	17
	CR 61 Jan. 1979	11" Cakeplate		3510 SC	40
		9" Bowl		3524 SC	22
		10" Basket		3537 SC	45
		8" Vase		3551 SC	22
		4" Vase		3554 SC	12
		Candleholder		3570 SC	23/pr.
		Footed Candy Box		3580 SC	40
	CR 62 Jan. 1977	Fairy Light	Owl	5108 RE	35
		Bowl	Basket Weave	8222 RE	30
		Bowl	Leaf & Orange Tree	8223 RE	50
		Planter Bowl	Floral	8226 RE	80
		Comport	Flowered	8422 RE	50
		7" Basket	Threaded w/Diamond Optic	8435 RE	60
		Footed Candy Box	Water lily	8480 RE	75
		Cov'd Candy Box on Base	Ogee	9394 RE	95
	CR 63 Jan. 1977	8" Plate	Leaf	5116 RE	35
		Swan		5127 RE	28
		Happiness Bird		5197 RE	30
		Bonbon	Butterfly	8230 RE	35
		Fairy Light	Heart	8406 RE	65
		Ceremonial Light	Chou Ting	8407 RE	80
		3-Toed Bowl	Water lily	8426 RE	35
		Bell	Faberge	8466 RE	35
		Candleholder	Water lily	8473 RE	60/pr.
		Bud Vase		9056 RE	30
		Bowl	Carolina Dogwood	9424 RE	45
		Candy Box	Chessie	9480 RE	275
113	CR 64 Jan. 1979	Fairy Light	Roses H/P	1700 RD	25
		Happiness Bird		5197 RD	25

		Hammered Colonial Lamp, 16"		7204 RD	175
		7" Basket		7237 RD	40
		4-1/2" Vase		7254 RD	18
		Candy Box		7484 RD	30
		Medallion Bell		8267 RD	25
		Bud Vase		9056 RD	25
	CR 65 Jan. 1979	Fairy Light	Love (Roses H/P)	1700 LR	28
		Fairy Light		7300 LW	35
		Bell		7362 LR, LW	25, 25
		Bud Vase		9056 LR, LW	17, 17
		25th Anniversary Plate		9417 SL	24
	CR 66 Jan. 1975	Footed Comport	Violets in the Snow on Spanish Lace	3522 DV	20
		9" Bowl		3524 DV	28
		8-1/2" Basket		3538 DV	43
		8" Vase		3551 DV	34
		4" Vase		3554 DV	17
		Bell		3567 DV	25
		Candleholder		3570 DV	35/pr.
		Footed Candy Box		3580 DV	40
	CR 67 Jan. 1975	Praying Girl & Boy		5100 WS	38/pr.
		Happiness Bird		5197 WS	25
		9" Bowl	Water lily	8424 WS	20
		Candleholder		8473 WS	20/pr.
		Ashtray, Candle Bowl or Chip 'n Dip		8478 WS	12
		Candy Box		8480 WS	20
		Footed Comport		8481 WS	14
		Jardiniere		8498 WS	20
		Bell	Madonna	9467 WS	10
		Anniversary Plate		9416 BL, GL, SL	18, 18, 18
		Anniversary Plate		9417 SL	24
114	CR 68 Jan. 1976	6" Vase	Daisies on Custard	7256 DC	20
		Candy or Puff Box		7480 DC	35
		Medallion Bell		8267 DC	25
		Medallion Candy Box		8288 DC	30
		Bud Vase		9056 DC	18
		19-1/2" Student Lamp		9308 DC	155
	CR 69 July 1978	Swan	Daisies on Cameo	5161 CD	22
		Bunny		5162 CD	26
		Small Bird		5163 CD	25
		Happiness Bird		5197 CD	28
		16" Hammered Colonial Lamp		7204 CD	150
		21" Student Lamp		7209 CD	175
		7" Basket		7237 CD	32
		7" Vase		7252 CD	30
		4-1/2" Vase		7254 CD	15
		Fairy Light		7300 CD	30
		Footed Comport		7429 CD	25
		Medallion Bell		8267 CD	25
		Bud Vase		9056 CD	20

	CR 70 Jan. 1974	Footed Nut Dish	Pink Blossom	7229 PY	20
		21" Student Lamp		7410 PY	195
		Footed Comport		7429 PY	30
		Pitcher		7461 PY	32
	CR 71 Jan. 1974	Egg	Pink Blossom	5140 PY	30
		Happiness Bird		5197 PY	28
		7" Vase		7252 PY	50
		Fairy Light		7300 PY	30
		Candy Box		7380 PY	30
		10" Hurricane Light		7409 PY	80
		Basket		7437 PY	42
115	CR 72 July 1979	16" Hammered Colonial Lamp	Christmas Classic	7204 NC	195
		Fairy Light		7300 NC	35
		8" Plate		7418 NC	25
		Bell		7466 NC	35
	CR 73 Jan. 1979	Happiness Bird	Cardinals in Winter	5197 CW	28
		16" Hammered Colonial Lamp		7206 CW	200
		7" Basket		7237 CW	45
		7" Vase		7252 CW	30
		4-1/2" Vase		7254 CS	15
		Fairy Light		7300 CW	30
		Medallion Bell		8267 CW	25
		19-1/2" Student Lamp		9308 CW	175
		Bud Vase		9056 CW	20
	CR 74 Jan. 1977	7" Basket	Butterflies on Milk Glass	7237 BY	32
		7" Vase		7252 PY	50
		4-1/2" Vase		7254 PY	15
		Fairy Light		7300 PY	30
		Medallion Bell		8267 PY	25
		Medallion Candy Box		8288 PY	30
		Bud Vase		9056 PY	18
		19-1/2" Student Lamp		9308 PY	155
	CR 75 Jan. 1979	Happiness Bird	Bluebirds on Custard	5197 BC	28
		7" Basket		7237 BC	40
		4-1/2" Vase		7254 BC	18
		10" Vase		7257 BC	32
		Fairy Light		7300 BC	35
		Medallion Bell		8267 BC	28
		Bud Vase		9056 BC	20
		20" Student Lamp		9308 BC	175
116	CR 76 Jan. 1971	11" Vase	Hobnail	3752 BR	175 S
		7" Vase	Undecorated	7252 BR	40
		7" Vase		7253 BR	85
		7" Pinch Vase		7359 BR	50
		Fairy Light (1 piece)		7392 BR	110
		8" Bowl		7422 BR	60
		Rose Bowl		7424 BR	70

		Basket		7437 BR	45
		Pitcher		7461 BR	60
		Cruet Vase		7462 BR	90
		2-piece Fairy Light		7492 BR	65
		5" Ribbed Vase		9055 BR	95
	CR 77 Jan. 1971	7" Vase	Maple Leaf Decal	7252 BD	65
		Fairy Light		7392 BD	150
		8" Bowl		7422 BD	90
		Rose Bowl		7424 BD	65
		Basket		7437 BD	100
		Pitcher		7461 BD	65
		Cruet Vase		7462 BD	90
		2-piece Fairy Light		7492 BD	65
	CR 78 Jan. 1971	7" Vase	Roses	7252 RB	75
		7" Vase		7253 RB	125
		7" Pinch Vase		7359 RB	65
		Fairy Light (1 piece)		7392 RB	200
		8" Bowl		7422 RB	125
		Rose Bowl		7424 RB	65
		Basket		7437 RB	95
		Pitcher		7461 RB	65
		Cruet Vase		7462 RB	95
		2-piece Fairy Light		7492 RB	65
	CR 79 Jan. 1977	Praying Boy & Girl		5100 CN	50/pr.
		Happiness Bird		5197 CN	28
		7" Basket	Threaded Diamond Optic	8435 CN	38
		Comport	Drape & Tie	8436 CN	25
		Bell	Faberge	8466 CN	25
		Bud Vase		9056 CN	20
		Bowl	Carolina Dogwood	9424 CN	30
		Candy Box	Madonna	9484 CN	30
117	CR 80 Jan. 1973	Boot	Daisy & Button	1990 CN	18
		8" Bowl	Holly	8220 CN	25
		Bowl	Persian Medallion	8224 CN	30
		Nappy	Grape	8225 CN	15
		Footed Bowl	Hearts & Flowers	8228 CN	40
		Cupped Bowl		8229 CN	40
		Handled Bonbon	Butterfly	8230 CN	25
		2-handled Footed Comport	Fruit	8231 CN	25
		Cupped Bowl	Orange Tree/Cherry	8232 CN	32
		3-Toed Nut Dish	Leaf	8235 CN	18
		Bowl	Daisy Pinwheel & Cable	8236 CN	27
		8-3/4" Bowl	Heart & Vine	8237 CN	18
		Tumbler	Butterfly & Berry	8240 CN	27
		Toothpick Holder	Panelled Daisy	8294 CN	12
		Toothpick Holder	Strawberry	8295 CN	12
		Oval Dish	Pansy	9125 CN	20
		Ring Tree	Turtle	9199 CN	35
	CR 81 Jan. 1973	Bell	Daisy & Button	1966 CN	18
		Candleholder	Swan	5172 CN	25
		Large Hen on Nest		5182 CN	70

		Small Hen on Nest		5186 CN	35
		Candy Box	Heart Shaped	8200 CN	105
		Bowl	Basket Weave	8222 CN	20
		Basket	Persian Medallion	8238 CN	37
		Chalice	Persian Medallion	8241 CN	27
		Swung Vase	Diamond Point & Column	8255 CN	24
		Swung Vase		8256 CN	18
		8" Vase	Peacock	8257 CN	65
		Candy Box	Daisy	9125 CN	20
		Comport	Rose	9222 CN	35
	CR 82 Jan. 1971	Boot	Daisy & Button	1990 CN	18
		Butterfly		5170 CN	35
		10-1/2"	Alley Cat	5177 CN	68
		Fish Paperweight		5193 CN	38
		3-Toed Bowl	Leaf & Orange Tree	8223 CN	25
		8" Bowl	Persian Medallion	8224 CN	30
		Planter Bowl		8226 CN	55
		Bowl	Hearts & Flowers	8229 CN	40
		Swung Vase	Dia. Pt. & Column	8255 CN	24
		8" Vase	Peacock	8257 CN	65
		Candy Box	Strawberry	9088 CN	55
		Tall Comport	Roses	9222 CN	35
	CR 83 Jan. 1975	Bell	Daisy & Button	1966 CN	18
		Candy Box	Pagoda	8201 CN	32
		Bowl	Leaf & Orange Tree	8223 CN	25
		Comport	Pinwheel	8227 CN	28
		Bowl	Orange Tree/Cherry	8233 CN	35
		Comport	Persian Medallion	8234 CN	25
		Footed Nut Dish	Scroll & Eye	8248 CN	18
		Toothpick Holder	Strawberry	8295 CN	12
		Comport	Pinwheel	8427 CN	22
		Bowl	Butterfly & Berry	8428 CN	25
		6" Candleholder	Orange Tree	8472 CN	40/pr.
		Candy Box	Wild Strawberry	9088 CN	55
		8" Vase	Scroll	9155 CN	35
		Candy Box	Daisy	9185 CN	32
		Comport	Rose	9222 CN	35
		Bell	Madonna	9467 CN	18
118	CR 84 Jan. 1977	Happiness Bird		5197 RN	35
		Candy Box	Pagoda	8201 RN	32
		Bowl	Leaf & Orange Tree	8223 RN	25
		Comport	Pinwheel	8227 RN	30
		Bowl	Butterfly & Berry	8428 RN	32
		Comport	Drape & Tie	8436 RN	30
		24" GWTW Lamp	Poppy	9101 RN	300
	CR 85 Jan. 1977	Ceremonial Light	Chou Ting	8407 RN	60
		Bowl	Basket Weave	8222 RN	25
		Comport	Persian Medallion	8234 RN	30
		Basket	Persian Medallion	8238 RN	40
		20" Student Lamp	Poppy	9107 RN	210
		8" Vase	Scroll	9155 RN	50

		Bowl	Carolina Dogwood	9424 RN	30
		Bell	Madonna	9467 RN	28
	CR 86 Jan. 1969	Candle Bowl	Hobnail	3872 BK, CA, CB, CG, MI	17, 17, 17 17, 17
	CR 87 Jan. 1973	Bell	Daisy & Button	1966 CO	18
		Boot	Daisy & Button	1990 CO	18
		Bowl	Leaf & Orange Tree	8223 CO	25
		Bowl	Persian Medallion	8224 CO	32
		Nappy	Grape	8225 CO	15
		Comport	Pinwheel	8227 CO	30
		Cupped Bowl	Hearts & Flowers	8229 CO	40
		Bonbon, Handled	Butterfly	8230 CO	25
		Handled Footed Comport	Fruit	8231 CO	30
		Comport	Persian Medallion	8234 CO	25
		Flared Bowl	Orange Tree	8239 CO	32
		Toothpick Holder	Strawberry	8295 CO	12
		Candy Box	Wild Strawberry	9088 CO	55
		Candy Box	Daisy	9185 CO	27
119	CR 88 Jan. 1971	Rabbit		5174 CN	60
		Owl		5178 CN	65
		Large Hen on Nest		5182 CN	70
		Plate	Persian Medallion	8219 CN	20
		Bowl	Basket Weave/Open Edge	8222 CN	20
		Comport	Pinwheel	8227 CN	28
		Oval Dish	Pansy	9125 CN	20
		Candy Box	Panelled Daisy	9185 CN	32
	CR 89 Jan. 1971	Bell	Daisy & Button	1966 CN	18
		Vase	Atlantis	5150 CN	85
		Candleholder	Swan	5172 CN	25/ea.
		Small Hen on Nest		5186 CN	35
		8" Bowl	Holly	8220 CN	25
		Nappy	Grape Cluster	8225 CN	15
		Flared Bowl	Hearts & Flowers	8228 CN	40
		3-Toed Nut Dish	Leaf	8235 CN	18
		Planter Vase	Mermaid	8254 CN	75
		Swung Vase		8256 CN	18
		Toothpick	Strawberry	8295 CN	12
		Craftsman Plate	Printer	9116 CN, BA, WS	24
		Candy Box	Panelled Daisy	9185 CN	32
	CR 90 Jan. 1978	Swan		5161 CN	24
		Bunny		5162 CN	28
		Small Bird		5163 CN	25
		Fairy Light	Beaded	8405 CN	30
		Bowl	Curtain	8454 CN	25
		3-Toed Vase	Grape	8457 CN	25
		Mother's Day Plate	The Madonna	9378 CN, BA, WS	17, 15, 12
		Candy Box	Baroque	9388 CN	30
	CR 91 Jan. 1979	Bell	Lily of the Valley	8285 CN	20
		Oval Basket		8437 CN	30
		Rose Bowl		8453 CN	23

		Bud Vase		8458 CN	12
		Footed Candy Box		8484 CN	35
		Mother's Day Plate	Madonna of the Rose Hedge	9379 CN	17
120	CR 92 Jan. 1975	Patriot's Bell		8467 PR	30
		Eagle Paperweight		8470 PR	30
		Jefferson Comport		8476 PR	145
		Eagle Plate		9418 PR	32
	CR 93 Jan. 1979	Craftsman Plate	The Cabinetmaker	9179 CN	20
		Craftsman Stein	Glassmaker	9640 CN	25
		Craftsman Bell		9660 CN	27
	CR 94 Jan. 1974	Vase	Love Bird	8258 CB	25
		Cream & Sugar	Millersburg Cherries	8402 CN	30/pr.
		Oval Comport	Pinwheel	8427 CN	22
		Bowl	Butterfly & Berry	8428 CN	25
		6" Candleholder	Orange Tree	8472 CN	40/pr.
		Craftsman Plate	Cooper	9119 CN	25
		8" Vase	Swirl	9155 CN	35
		Mother's Day Plate	Madonna of the Grotto	9319 CN, BA, WS	17, 15, 12
121	CR 95 Jan. 1979	Fairy Light	Cameo Opal Spiral	3100 CO	40
		Basket		3137 CO	45
		6-1/2" Vase		3157 CO	22
		44 Oz. Pitcher		3164 CO	45
		10 Oz. Pitcher		3166 CO	28
		Candy Box		3180 CO	48
		Nappy	Grape	8225 CO	15
		Nut Dish	Scroll & Eye	8248 CO	18
		Toothpick	Panelled Daisy	8294 CO	15
		Comport	Water Lily	8431 CO	28
		Bowl	Curtain	8454 CO	25
	CR 96 Jan. 1979	Fairy Light	Hobnail	3608 CO	18
		Footed Comport		3628 CO	14
		Bell		3667 CO	12
		Margarine Tub or Candy Box		3802 CO	20
		7" Basket		3837 CO	25
		4-1/2" Vase		3854 CO	10
		26" Lamp		3907 CO	190
		10" Bud Vase		3950 CO	10
	CR 97 Jan. 1978	Fairy Light	Hobnail	3608 BO	20
		Ashtray Set		3610 BO	35/set
		Footed Comport		3628 BO	14
		Bell		3667 BO	15
		Bowl, Candy/Butter		3802 BO	22
		7" Basket		3837 BO	32
		26" Lamp		3907 BO	200
		Bud Vase		3950 BO	10
		Candleholder		3974 BO	28
	CR 98 Jan. 1978	Nappy	Grape	8225 BO	15
		Nut Dish	Scroll & Eye	8248 BO	15
		Bell	Lily of the Valley	8265 BO	25
		Toothpick	Panelled Daisy	8294 BO	15

		Comport	Water Lily	8431 BO	25
		Basket	Lily of the Valley	8437 BO	30
		Bowl	Curtain	8454 BO	20
		Candy Box	Panelled Daisy	9185 BO	25
122	CR 99 Jan. 1977	Praying Boy & Girl		5100 VE	30/pr.
		Happiness Bird		5197 VE	23
		Ceremonial Light	Chou Ting	8407 VE	30
		Bowl	Basket Weave	8222 VE	10
		Rose Bowl	Water Lily	8429 VE	20
		Footed Basket		8433 VE	40
		Bell	Faberge	8466 VE	15
		Footed Candy Box	Water Lily	8480 VE	25
	CR 100 Jan 1977	Light	Currier & Ives	8409 VE	25
		9" Bowl	Water Lily	8424 VE	30
		Footed Comport		8430 VE	15
		7" Basket		8434 VE	25
		Candleholder		8473 VE	30/pr.
		36 Oz. Pitcher		8464 VE	37
		Bride & Groom Bell w/Lovebirds		9168 VE	25
	CR 101 Jan. 1978	Swan		5161 VE	14
		Butterfly on Stand		5171 VE	28
		Fairy Light	Beaded	8405 VE	30
		Footed Bowl (crimped)	Water Lily	8423 VE	50
		3-Toed Basket	Grape	8438 VE	22
		Nut Dish	Lotus	8441 VE	8
		Bowl	Curtain	8454 VE	8
		Bud Vase	Water Lily	8456 VE	18
		22" Offset Colonial Lamp	Poppy	9403 VE	125
	CR 102 Jan. 1978	Bunny		5162 VE	22
		Small Bird		5163 VE	24
		Pelican Tray		5175 VE	35
		12-1/2" Cake Plate	Water Lily	8410 VE	45
		Footed Bowl (Cupped)		8439 VE	24
		3-Toed Vase	Grape	8457 VE	18
		Candy Box	Baroque	9388 VE	24
		21" Student Lamp	Poppy	9405 VE	127
123	CR 103 Jan. 1979	Praying Boy & Girl		5100 VE	30/pr.
		Prayer Light	Madonna	5107 VE	30
		Bowl	Basket Weave	8222 VE	10
		Rose Bowl	Water Lily	8429 VE	20
		Footed Basket	Water Lily	8433 VE	40
		Bud Vase	Water Lily	8456 VE	18
		Bell	Faberge	8466 VE	15
		Footed Candy Box	Water Lily	8480 VE	25
	CR 104 Jan. 1979	Light	Currier & Ives	8409 VE	25
		9" Bowl	Water Lily	8424 VE	30
		7" Basket	Water Lily	8434 VE	25
		Bowl	Curtain	8454 VE	8
		36 Oz. Pitcher	Water Lily	8464 VE	37

		Candleholder		8473 VE	26/pr.
		Bell	Bride & Groom	9168 VE	25
	CR 105 Jan. 1979	Swan		5161 VE	14
		Bunny		5162 VE	22
		Small Bird		5163 VE	24
		Turtle		5164 VE	20
		Cat		5165 VE	23
		Frog		5166 VE	20
		Sunfish		5167 VE	24
		Butterfly on Stand		5171 VE	28
		Happiness Bird		5197 VE	23
		3-Toed Basket	Grape	8438 VE	22
		Nut Dish	Lotus	8441 VE	8
		3-Toed Vase	Grape	8457 VE	18
		Craftsman Stein	Glass Blower	9640 VE	25
		Craftsman Bell	Glass Blower	9660 VE	22
	CR 106 Jan. 1980	Owl		5168 VE	20
		Oval Comport	Pinwheel	8427 VE	25
		Ring Tree	Owl	9299 VE	8
		Fairy Light	Strawberry	9407 VE	20
		7" Bowl		9427 VE	8
		Comport		9428 VE	10
		7" Basket		9437 VE	25
		Bud Vase		9454 VE	8
		Bell		9465 VE	15
124	CR 107 Jan. 1980	8" Plate	"Sunset"	7418 SS	40
		Basket		7437 SS	42
		Bell	"New Born"	5564 NB	
	CR 108 Jan. 1980	8" Plate	"New Born"	7418 NB	25
		Bell		7564 NB	30
		Bud Vase	Roses—H/P	9056 AS	
	CR 109 Jan. 1980	Collecti—Bells	Knobby Bull's Eye	9061 CO	22
			Grape	9062 CO	22
			Sydenham	9063 CO	22
			Whittoon	9064 FO	22
			Sable Arche	9065 TO	32
	CR 110 Jan. 1980	Bell	Lily of the Valley	8265 TO	28
		Fairy Light		8404 TO	35
		Oval Basket		8437 TO	37
		Handkerchief Vase		8450 TO	20
		Bud Vase		8458 TO	15
		Candleholder		8475 TO	38/pr.
		Footed Candy Box		8484 TO	40
		Candy Box		8489 TO	32
125	CR 111 Jan. 1980	Praying Boy & Girl		5100 PK	30
		Bunny		5162 PK	28
		Small Bird		5163 PK	24
		Cat		5165 PK	24
		Owl		5168 PK	20

		Item	Decoration	No.	Price
		Temple Jar		7488 PK	25
		2-Piece Fairy Light		7500 PK	28
		Rolled Rim Bowl		7523 PK	20
		Comport		7528 PK	15
		Nut Dish		7529 PK	12
		7" Basket		7537 PK	35
		7" Vase		7550 PK	25
		10" Vase		7557 PK	25
		Bell		7564 PK	25
		Candleholder		7572 PK	25/pr.
		Tall Temple Jar		7588 PK	40
		Mandarin Vase		8251 PK	50
		Empress Vase		8252 PK	45
		Tall Bud Vase		9054 PK	15
	CR 112 Jan. 1980	Praying Boy & Girl		5100 JA	30
		Bunny		5162 JA	28
		Small Bird		5163 JA	24
		Cat		5165 JA	24
		Owl		5168 JA	20
		Temple Jar		7488 JA	25
		Two-Piece Fairy Light		7500 JA	28
		Rolled Rim Bowl		7523 JA	20
		Comport		7528 JA	15
		Nut Dish		7529 JA	12
		7" Basket		7537 JA	35
		7" Vase		7550 JA	25
		10" Vase		7557 JA	25
		Bell		7564 JA	25
		Candleholder		7572 JA	25/pr.
		Tall Temple Jar		7588 JA	40
		Mandarin Vase		8251 JA	50
		Empress Vase		8252 JA	45
		Tall Bud Vase		9054 JA	15
126	CR 113 Jan. 1980	16" Hammered Colonial Lamp			
			"Sunset" on Cameo	7204 SS	175
		21" Student Lamp		7209 SS	225
		4-1/2" Vase		7254 SS	25
		Tulip Vase		7255 SS	45
		Two-Piece Fairy Light		7300 SS	35
		8" Plate		7418 SS	40
		Basket		7437 SS	42
		Temple Jar		7488 SS	35
		Bell		7564 SS	42
	CR 114 Jan. 1980	Swan	Blue Dogwood on Cameo	5161 BD	20
		Bunny		5162 BD	26
		Small Bird		5163 BD	25
		Cat		5165 BD	25
		Happiness Bird		5197 BD	30
		16" Hammered Colonial Lamp		7204 BD	175
		Nut Dish		7229 BD	17

		7" Vase		7252 BD	85/45
		Fairy Light		7300 BD	35
		Hurricane Lamp		7312 BD	110
		Bottle		7363 BD	60
		Footed Comport		7429 BD	30
		Candy Box		7484 BD	35
		Temple Jar		7488 BD	35
		Bud Vase		9056 BD	20
127	CR 115 Jan. 1980	Oval Bowl	Daisy & Button	1921 CY	15
		10-1/2" Bowl		1925 CY	15
		Bell		1967 CY	10
		Candleholder		1970 CY	20/pr.
		8-1/2" Covered Bowl		1987 CY	28
		Slipper		1995 CY	12
		2-Piece Fairy Light	Fine Cut & Block	9102 CY	20
		Covered Sugar & Cream		9103 CY	30
		Salt & Pepper		9106 CY	15
		Comport		9120 CY	12
		7" Bowl		9127 CY	10
		7" Basket		9137 CY	20
		Goblet		9143 CY	15
		Small Bud Vase		9150 CY	10
		4-1/2" Vase		9157 CY	10
		Swung Vase		9158 CY	8
		Tall Handkerchief Vase		9159 CY	15
		Candle Bowl		9172 CY	25
		Candy Box		9180 CY	20
	CR 117 Jan. 1980	Bell	H/P Blue Dogwood on Cameo	7564 BD	28
		Tall Bud Vase		9054 BD	18
		10" Student Lamp (Basketweave)		9305 BD	180
		Vase		9324 BD	25
		7" Basket		9334 BD	35
	CR 118 Jan. 1980	Comport	Hobnail	3628 CN	15
		Bell		3667 CN	18
		Oval Candy Box		3786 CN	25
		Toothpick		3795 CN	12
		7" Basket		3837 CN	38
		4-1/2" Vase		3854 CN	15
		Cat		5165 CN	25
		Owl		5168 CN	28
		Craftsman Plate	The Tanner	9680 CN	15
128	CR 119 June 1980	16" Hammered Colonial Lamp Christmas Classics "Going Home"		7204 GH	175
		2-Piece Fairy Light		7300 GH	45
		8" Plate		7418 GH	35
		Bell		7466 GH	35
	CR 120 June 1980	Footed Comport	Hobnail	F3628 BO	NA
		Bud Vase	Hobnail	F3950 CO	NA
		Vase	Hobnail	F3752 MI	NA

		Praying Boy & Girl		F5100 WS, VE	NA
		Swan		F5161 VE	NA
		Small Bird		F5163 VE	NA
		Cat		F5165 VE	NA
		Owl		F5168 VE	NA
		Butterfly		F5171 VE	NA
		Nappy	Grape	F8225 BO	NA
		Footed Comport	Scroll & Eye	F8248 CO	NA
		Bell	Lily of the Valley	F8265 BO	NA
		Oval Basket		F8437 CO	NA
		Small Handkerchief Vase		F8450 BO	NA
		GWTW Lamp	Poppy	F9101 MI	NA
	CR 121 June 1980	Christmas Plate	Christ Church	8280 CN, BA, WS	20, 20, 20
	CR 122 June 1980	Fairy Light	H/P Holly	1700 CH, RH	25
		Medallion Bell		8267 CH, RH	25
		2-Piece Fairy Light	Nativity	9401 VE, AW, TB	25
		Bell	Nativity	FL,VE, AW, TB	20,20,20
129	CR 123 and 124	11" Lamp	Currier & Ives		
	June 1980		"The Old Grist Mill"	8400 TB, TN,	130
				VE, AW	125, 125
		Fairy Light/Vase		8409 TB, TN,	30, 30
				VE, AW	25, 20
		8" Plate		8418 TB, TN,	20, 20
				VE, AW	20, 20
		Bell		8461 TB, TN,	20, 20
				VE, AW	18, 20
	CR 125 June 1980	5-Piece Epergne		7505 VR	200
		Salver	Velva Rose	7516 VR	18
		6-1/2" Bowl		7526 VR	15
		Footed Comport		7527 VR	24
		Nut Dish		7529 VR	14
		8-1/2" Basket		7536 VR	28
		Fan Vase	Dolphin	7551 VR	25
		Bell (Star Crimped)		7562 VR	30
		Candleholder		7472 VR	NA
		Candy Box, Covered	Dolphin	7580 VR	30
		3-Piece Fairy Light	Persian Medallion	8408 VR	40
		Bud Vase		9056 VR	17
		Comport	Persian Medallion	9422 VR	25
130	CR 126 1961	Covered Sugar & Cream	Hobnail	3608 MI	20
		6-1/2" Basket		3736 MI	25
		Bud Vase		3756 MI	12
		Oval Candy Box		3786 MI	20
		Salt & Pepper		3806 MI	15/pr.
		Slipper		3995 MI	10
	CR 127 1962	3" Vase	Hobnail	3853 MI	8
		6" Vase		3856 MI	18
		8" Vase	"Wheat" Silver Crest	5859 SC	35
	CR 128 1963	3-Piece Vanity Set	Hobnail	3805 MI	NA

		on Vanity Tray		3775 MI	28/pr.
		Courting Lamps	Diamond Optic	1791 CB, CA	NA
	CR 129 1964	7" Basket		7237 SC	32
131	CR 130 1969	Boudoir Lamp		3604 MI	200
		Fairy Light		3608 MI	18
		Handled Bonbon	Hobnail	3706 MI	18
		Candle Bowl		3873 MI	15
		Footed Comport	Hobnail	3886 MI	25
		Covered Sugar & Cream	Hobnail	3902 MI	28
		Decision Maker	Owl	5180 BK, MI	35, 25
		7" Vase	Violets in the Snow	7252 DV	45
		8" Vase		7258 DV	38
		Candleholder		7271 DV	38/pr.
		9-1/2" Bowl	Silver Crest	7423 WC	35
		6-1/2" Basket		7436 SC	28
		10" Vase		7458 DV	85
		Pitcher		7464 DV	40
		Candy Box	Strawberry	9088 MI	30
	CR 131 Jan. 1969	5-1/2" Bonbon	Violets in the Snow	7225 DV	DV
		5" Top Hat		7292 DV	65
		Low Footed Comport		7329 DV	20
		Heart Shaped Relish		7333 DV	30
		6-1/2" Handled Basket		7336 DV	40
		Footed Comport D.C.		7429 DV	39
		Small Basket		7436 DV	40
		6" Vase		7451 DV	28
		Handled Bonbon		7498 DV	25
	CR 132 Jan. 1972	Covered Jam or Candy	Hobnail H/P Blue Bells	3600 BB	45
		Candleholder	Hobnail	3775 MI	28/pr.
		Toothpick Holder	Hobnail H/P BlueBells	3795 BB	10
		8-1/2" Fan Vase		3852 BB	95
		10" Bud Vase	Hobnail	3950 MI	15
		Handkerchief Vase		3951 MI	28
		7" Vase		3954 MI	20
		Tall Bud Vase	Black w/H/P White Daisies	4453 WD	28
		8" Footed Vase		4454 WD	32
		Bud Vase		4455 WD	20
		Ashtray		4469 WD	18
		Cruet w/Stopper	Roses H/P	7468 RB	110
		Cruet w/Stopper	Maple Leaf Decal	7468 BD	150
	CR 133 1967	GWTW Lamp	Roses	9205 WR, OB	350
		GWTW Lamp		9207 HA, OB	155, 215
		Student Lamp	Roses	9208 MI	120

OLDE VIRGINIA GLASS

Item	Ware Number	Value and Rarity
Milk Glass Lavabo	A	75.00
Hurricane Lamps	B	70.00 R
9-Piece Beverage Set	C	225.00/set
Footed Covered Compote	D	35.00
Footed Nut Dish	E	12.00
Epergne	F	35.00
Footed Banana Bowl	G	20.00
Footed Cakeplate	H	35.00
Lacework Compote	J	20.00
2-Piece Cheese Dip	K	20.00
Planter Plate	L	35.00 R
Vase	1050 CA, CG	15.00
	1050 CB	20.00
	1050 OR	25.00
Sugar & Cream	1903 MI	15.00/pr.
Salt & Pepper	1906 MI	15.00/pr.
Oval Bowl	1921 BG, CT, MI	15.00
Bowl	1925 MI	15.00
Oval Bowl	1929 MI	17.00
Basket	1930 MI	27.00
Basket	1935 MI	20.00
Vase	1958 MI	20.00
Fan Vase	1959 MI	22.00
Bell	1967 BG, CT, MI	12.00
Candleholder	1970 BG, CT, MI	15.00/pr.
Hat	1992 CN	15.00
	1992 MI	10.00
Bootee	1994 CN	25.00
	1994 MI	12.00
Slipper	1995 CN	20.00
	1995 BG, CT, MI	15.00
Colonial Vase	2462 CA, CB	18.00
Oil Courting Lamp	2490 CA	65.00
Courting Lamp	2491 CA	58.00
Student Lamp	2807 BG, CT, MI	100.00
9-Piece Beverage Set	3811	225.00/set
4-Piece Epergne Set	4401 MI	55.00
5-Piece Breakfast Set	4402 MI	45.00
Sugar & Creamer	4403 MI	20.00
Chip 'n Dip	4404 MI	45.00
2-Piece Chip 'n Dip	4404 MI	45.00
Hanging Planter	4405 MI	75.00 R
15-Piece Punch Set	4406 MI	275.00/set
Salt & Pepper Set	4408 MI	12.00/pr.
Footed Cakeplate	4413 MI	37.00
Round Bowl	4427 MI	20.00
Footed Nut Dish	4428 MI	12.00
Footed Comport	4429 MI	10.00

Oval Basket	4430 MI	30.00
Handled Basket	4437 MI	27.00
Basket	4438 MI	27.00
Goblet	4445 MI	9.00
Bud Vase	4456 MI	8.00
Lavabo	4467 MI	75.00
Candleholders	4473 MI	40.00/pr.
Low Candleholder	4474 MI	23.00/pr.
Covered Candy Jar	4480 MI	30.00
Covered Compote	4484 MI	42.00
Oval Candy Box	4486 MI	12.00
Planter	4490 MI	28.00
2-Tier Tidbit	4494	30.00
Square Planter	4497 MI	18.00
Hurricane Lamps	4498	95.00 R
Epergne	4801	55.00
Bird Ashtray	5173 CA, CG, MI	30.00
	5173 CB, OR	35.00
Duck Ashtray	5175 MI	20.00
	5175 CA, CG	25.00
	5175 CB, OR	35.00
Lacework Compote	9020	35.00
Candy Box	9054 MI	30.00
Candy Box	9064 CB, OR	35.00
Candy Box	9084 CA, CG	30.00
Fairy Light with Candle	9102 BG, CT, MI	25.00
Sugar & Cream Set	9103 BG, CT, MI	20.00/pr.
Salt & Pepper	9106 BG, CT, MI	17.00/pr.
Compote	9120 CN	20.00
	9120 BG, CT, MI	12.00
Footed Bowl	9122 BG, CT, MI	14.00
Bowl	9127 BG, CT, MI	15.00
Basket	9137 BG, CT, MI	25.00
Candy Box	9150 CN	22.00
Footed Nut Dish	9151 CN	15.00
Swung Vase	9152 MI	15.00
Vase	9157 BG, CT, MI	10.00
Swung Vase	9158 CN	17.00
	9158 BG, CT, MI	12.00
Candle Bowl	9172 MI	15.00
Candy Box	9180 BG, CT, MI	22.00